HARMONIOUS HORSEMANSHIP

HARMONIOUS
HORSEMANSHIP

SUE DYSON AND SUE PALMER

Matador
Unit E2 Airfield Business Park,
Harrison Road, Market Harborough,
Leicestershire. LE16 7UL
Tel: 0116 2792299
Email: books@troubador.co.uk
Web: www.troubador.co.uk/matador
Twitter: @matadorbooks

ISBN 978 1805140 078

British Library Cataloguing in Publication Data.
A catalogue record for this book is available from the British Library.

Typeset in 12pt Minion Pro by Troubador Publishing Ltd, Leicester, UK

Matador is an imprint of Troubador Publishing Ltd

In loving memory of dad, forever in my heart.
Sue (Palmer)

To my horses, most especially McGinty, Kinvarra and Otterburn,
who taught me so much.
Sue (Dyson)

Thea Roberts

Table of contents

Harmonious Horsemanship: Use of the Ridden Horse Ethogram to Optimise Potential, Partnership and Performance

GUEST CONTRIBUTORS

Organisations

- Chapter 2:
  Human Behaviour Change for Animals (HBCA)

- Chapter 6:
  British Equine Veterinary Association (BEVA)
  Register of Animal Musculoskeletal Practitioners (RAMP)
  Association of Chartered Physiotherapists in Animal Therapy (ACPAT)
  Association of Animal Osteopaths (AAO)
  McTimoney Chiropractic Association (MCA)
  Society of Master Saddlers (SMS)

- Chapter 7:
  Saddle Research Trust (SRT)

Individuals

- Chapter 1:
Dr Rosie Jones-McVey PhD
Dr Lynda Birke PhD

- Chapter 2:
Dr Jo Hockenhull PhD

- Chapter 3:
Dr Jessica Mullard BSc BVetMed

- Chapter 4:
Dr Tamzin Furtado PhD

- Chapter 5:
Dr Jessica Kidd BA DVM CertES(Orth) Diplomate ECVS MRCVS RCVS European Recognised Specialist in Equine Surgery (Veterinary medicine)
Sonya Nightingale MCSP (Physiotherapy)
Dr Vav Simon DV AMC FRCC (Chiropractic)
Eleanor Andrews M.Ost, D.O. Animal Osteopathy, PGCertHE, PGCert. Paediatric Osteopathy (Osteopathy)
Mark Aikens DipWCF FdSc BSc(Hons) (Farriery)
Ellie Tomlinson Master Saddler and SMS Qualified Saddle Fitter (Saddlery)
Grant Chanter EDT (Dentistry)
Clare Macleod MSc RNutr (Nutrition)
Mary Wanless BSc BHSI (Coaching)
Boo Riley (Riding and Training)
Kelly Marks (Horsemanship)

Case Studies

- Chapter 1:
Alice and Star
Kathy and Devine

- Chapter 2:
  Hannah and Brio
  Hayley and Jacko

- Chapter 4:
  Rachel and Copper (names changed for anonymity)
  Claire and Digger

- Chapter 5:
  Thea and Jonny
  Heidi and Ricky

- Chapter 6:
  Anne and Sam
  Joanne and Ripley

- Chapter 7:
  Giselle and Mickey

Foreword

As a coach, international judge and former 5* level event rider my aim is to promote a harmonious, confident, trusting and happy relationship between horses and their riders. This book supports those ideals and has been written by two hugely knowledgeable, experienced and passionate people who care about horse wellbeing and the relationship and communication between horses and all those involved in their care.

Sue Palmer draws on a lifetime's experience of working with a broad cross-section of horses. She shows a genuine desire which shines through this book to help not only horses, but also their riders, carers, and support team. A short quote from the book for me says it all:

'I hope that one day, to overcome performance and behaviour problems, riders, trainers, coaches and all other equestrian professionals will first look for physical issues in the horse, rather than simply training the horse or the rider whilst ignoring the horse's attempt to communicate.'

A heart-warming thought, that in this day and age is much needed.

I first met Sue Dyson many years ago, in my quest to help one of my advanced event horses that had a minor problem and had been referred to Sue for further investigation. I was totally impressed and have since had help from her with competition horses several times over the years.

As Sue came into the equine veterinary profession with a history of riding in the three main Olympic disciplines, and also from an instructing background, one can clearly feel and see the passion she has for her work with our wonderful equine partners. She cares not only about the welfare of the horse, but also has the desire to help riders improve their knowledge and ability to recognise if their horse may be in some form of pain, that although minor, can still be the cause/ reason why the horse is perhaps less inclined or less able to perform how the rider wishes.

The book introduces the vast amount of research that has been done over recent years in order both to help us understand how horses can communicate with us and to enable us to recognise important behaviours. It also includes some real-life scenarios of horses and riders that are interesting to read and bring the book to life, with situations that we can all relate to.

This book serves as an inspiration to us all, to those who desire to understand how a horse can 'communicate' with humans and thus help us to 'hear' what the animal is trying to tell us, so that we can help horses and their riders.

The book is simply a must read for those who care about their beloved horse, and also for those of us who are passionate about helping to keep, and even improve 'Our Social License to ride and compete, and to ensure that riding horses remains palatable to the general public'. This is a hugely important factor in the current climate, and we all share responsibility for playing our part. We know that our goal is for horses to be well-ridden and totally happy in their work in whatever equestrian sphere they are performing. It's time we let the world know how much horses mean to us, and just how far we will go to ensure harmonious horsemanship.

Happy reading and even happier riding.

Andrew Bennie, Fellow of the British Horse Society

The Why, What, How, When And Where Of The Ridden Horse Pain Ethogram

Why: Because horses matter
What: We can recognise pain in ridden horses
How: By using the Ridden Horse Pain Ethogram
Where: Throughout the world
When: Now

"*Recognising pain in ridden horses is a subject close to both our hearts. Since you have chosen to pick this book up, we know that it's also close to your heart. Each of us has our own story as to why this is the case. In this preface we would like to share with you what has brought each of us to the point of writing this book.*

We fear that our 'right to ride' (social license) is at risk, and we believe that the time to act is now. We understand that recognising pain through ridden behaviour is a contentious issue, with widely varying viewpoints. All too often, 'bad behaviour' or 'poor performance' are seen as 'normal', or blamed on the rider, the saddle, the coach, the environment, anything other than the horse being in pain. It is difficult for us to accept that a horse might be uncomfortable, and it can seem easier to 'fix' these other areas, than to find the root cause and relieve the discomfort. There is much tradition within equestrianism, myths are perpetuated, and changes are slow. Although some are not yet ready to hear it, the science around recognising pain through ridden behaviour is strong, and the evidence base is growing. You can use the Ridden Horse Pain Ethogram, also known as the Ridden Horse Performance Checklist, to recognise musculoskeletal pain in horses which are not obviously lame. Individuals and organisations throughout the world are beginning to understand this better, and the horse world is changing. That we can recognise pain in ridden horses is an opinion shared by many, across all fields of equestrianism, and at the highest levels.

We have chosen to share our knowledge through both our own words and through the stories of others, in their own words. In this book you will learn of the struggles of real people in recognising and addressing pain in their own horses. We hope that this helps you to feel more connected, and less alone, on your journey with your horse. There are also stories from professionals who work with horses, ideas from scientists who study horses and horse people, and opinions from organisations we trust. We know that you will connect with these stories, remember them, and discuss them with your friends. As you do, the message that we must get better at recognising pain in ridden horses will spread. This, in turn, will lead to more ethical horsemanship, and to the improvements in potential, partnership and performance, that horses and riders throughout the world deserve to enjoy."

Sue and Sue

STUDYING THE LINKS BETWEEN PAIN, PERFORMANCE AND BEHAVIOUR – BY SUE PALMER

Sue Palmer

He had a history of bolting. That's why I was called to help. Little did I know how that call would steer the course of my career.

After asking numerous questions, I began by watching the owner tack up and lunge the handsome bay gelding. I was in my early twenties, a British Horse Society Assistant Instructor (BHSAI, now known as BHS Stage 3 Coach in Complete Horsemanship) and an Intelligent Horsemanship Recommended Trainer. I had no experience or qualifications in terms of veterinary or physical therapy for horses. But I'd ridden since I was three years old. I'd been through Pony Club and Riding Club. I'd lived with and worked for a horse dealer. I had taught at a riding school for several years. I'd worked in polo and in racing. I'd competed at British Eventing, British Dressage and British Show Jumping. I'd seen a good few horses in my years, and this one didn't look right to me. On the lunge, his quarters were sloping to the inside far more on the right rein than they were on the left rein. I didn't know the specifics, but I figured that he ought to look the same on both reins. I explained to his owner what I was seeing and recommended that she get in touch with a vet or a physical therapist to check her horse out, before we approached the problem from a behavioural or training perspective. I felt that if the horse wasn't right physically, maybe this could contribute to or cause the bolting behaviour when he was ridden.

Right there, on that cold, damp day in Berkshire, began my journey of studying the links between pain and behaviour. I continued working as a rider, an instructor and an equine behaviourist. My A-levels and my studies with the Open University gave me the relevant grounding and I got a place at Kings College London to study a BSc (Hons) in Physiotherapy. I worked as a Physiotherapist in the National Health Service in the West Midlands and spent evenings and weekends working with horses. I went on to qualify as a human and equine Massage Therapist and then to study an MSc in Veterinary Physiotherapy at the Royal Veterinary College in London. Once qualified, I registered with the Association of Chartered Physiotherapists in Animal Therapy (ACPAT) and the Register of Animal Musculoskeletal Practitioners (RAMP).

I remember asking a lecturer at the Royal Veterinary College whether I could do my dissertation on how to recognise pain in horses. I wanted to put together a guide and tick list on how owners could recognise back pain in their horse. How naive I was in terms of scientific research! The lecturer told me that the subject area was much too big for an MSc dissertation. The desire to help owners recognise pain in their horses has never left me, though, and in 2016 I wrote 'Understanding Horse Performance: Brain, Pain or Training?'. That book is based on my professional experience, and is validated by 27 guest contributions, but as yet there is no peer reviewed, published research to back up the work (give me time!).

You can imagine how excited I was when I attended a Horses Inside Out Conference and listened to a lecture from Dr Sue Dyson titled 'Brain or Pain?'! Of course, I knew of Sue and her work as an expert in the diagnosis and treatment of lameness in the horse. Indeed, I had shadowed her previously in her work at the Animal Health Trust. I gave Sue a copy of my book, and we kept in touch. The germs of an idea finally coalesced in my mind into a book when the paper on the Ridden Horse Pain Ethogram (RHpE) was published in 2018. Some traumatic life experiences have slowed my writing and the publication of this book. It turns out, as is so often the case when fate intervenes, that this delay is beneficial to you, the reader, since the science supporting the RHpE continues to grow. This means that we're able to share more evidence-based knowledge with you now than we could have done a few years ago. Meanwhile, I continue to treat horses daily in my work as an ACPAT and RAMP Registered Chartered Physiotherapist, and to discuss the links between pain and behaviour with owners, trainers, and riders.

You know that a horse can only communicate pain or discomfort through their behaviour or performance. If your horse has been in discomfort ever since you have known the horse, then you might not see any changes in that behaviour or performance. This doesn't mean the problem is not pain related. It simply means that the pain has been there since you first met that horse. I hope that one day, to overcome performance and behaviour problems, riders, trainers, coaches and all other equestrian professionals will first look for physical problems in the horse, rather than simply training the horse or the rider whilst ignoring the horse's attempts to communicate. Only once pain and discomfort have been ruled out, with the RHpE as one of the tools used to do this, should the problem be dealt with through training.

WHY WAS THE RHPE CREATED? – BY SUE DYSON

I came to the equine veterinary profession as a rider, having trained and ridden horses to Advanced level eventing, Grade A showjumping and Medium level

Sue Dyson and Otterburn

dressage, and also as an instructor with the opportunity to observe many horse-rider combinations. I have always considered that evaluation of horses during ridden exercise was a crucial part of any lameness assessment, unless the horse was too lame to be ridden. I was aware, having ridden many of my clients' horses, that they often felt worse than they superficially appeared from the ground, and that their behaviour, 'rideability' and quality of movement could be transformed immediately if I removed their pain by using nerve blocks.

Furthermore, I had become progressively frustrated by the lack of recognition by riders and trainers that training or rideability problems usually reflected underlying pain. I was aware, through daily clinical observations, and through a variety of studies that we had performed involving sports and leisure horses in normal work and assumed to be working comfortably, that riders were poor at recognising lameness. I was continually exasperated when I acquired the history of clients' horses and realised that problems had long pre-dated the riders' awareness. For example, I was told that 'ever since I bought the horses three years ago, he has found canter on the left rein difficult', despite the owner first seeking help just one week previously. I was aware that long-term problems are far more difficult to fix than recent onset problems because the horses develop so many secondary adaptations of movement, lose muscle mass, and develop a restricted range of motion that is difficult to restore.

It was essential to try to introduce a new way of guiding riders, coaches and trainers to become aware that a horse may have underlying pain manifest by abnormal behaviour and make people aware that behaviours such as ears back, mouth opening and tail swishing are not normal for pain-free horses. I hoped that education about behaviour might be more easily taught than lameness recognition.

Likewise, I was aware that many veterinarians have received limited training in lameness diagnosis, no training in how to assess horses while ridden and little training in equine behaviour. Yet, there seemed to be a conviction that if lameness could not be seen in hand or on the lunge then the horse was not lame, and therefore any problem encountered during ridden exercise must be likely to be behavioural in origin.

Things came to a head when a valuable event horse with multiple problems was the subject of an insurance claim, supported by me, for permanent incapacity as an Advanced three-day event horse. A renowned veterinarian acting on behalf of the insurance company advised that the claim should not be accepted, and further treatments should be carried out. Against my better judgement, I gave additional treatments, but the horse was progressively deteriorating. I sent sequential video recordings of the horse to demonstrate the horse's demise and ultimately, after some strong letters, the claim was finally accepted. I was shocked that the veterinarian advising the insurance company apparently failed to recognise the level of discomfort that this horse had been experiencing, reflected by both its behaviour and gait abnormalities.

Finally, I submitted a paper to the Equine Veterinary Journal describing the clinical features of 46 horses with idiopathic (meaning we do not know what the cause is) hopping-type forelimb lameness in ridden horses, which I asserted was associated with pain because of the behavioural signs that I observed in association with the lameness. I acknowledged that affected horses were not improved by nerve blocks. In fact, some became worse, and phenylbutazone, a non-steroidal anti-inflammatory analgesic (pain relieving) drug, did not improve the lameness. The paper was accompanied by photographs and short video footage of some of the horses. Any paper has to undergo a peer review process by scientists with knowledge of the subject before it is accepted for publication. The reviewers rejected the paper, saying that they did not believe that the condition was induced by pain. I was incandescent, but also disturbed by the failure of so-called experts to recognise obvious signs of pain.

Serendipitously, I met Dr Jeannine Berger on a ski lift in Lake Tahoe, Nevada, USA. Jeannine is a veterinarian and a rider who is a Diplomate of both the American College of Veterinary Behaviour and the American College of Veterinary Welfare. I discussed these problems with her, shared video recordings of the hopping horses, and she was sure that the lameness was pain induced. As a result, we agreed that we would collaborate in research to ultimately produce and verify the use of the Ridden Horse Pain Ethogram.

What followed was a collaboration between me and Jeannine, supported by a small grant from World Horse Welfare. My then intern, Jessica Mullard, had developed an interest in ridden horse behaviour during the one-year internship, and she was persuaded to stay on for six months, on a miserly stipend, to work on the project. Through a friend, I was introduced to Dr Andrea Ellis, an equine scientist with statistical expertise and an interest in equine behaviour. The team was committed, had mutually complimentary skills, enthusiasm and drive, and worked first on facial expressions and then on the whole horse ethogram, a great collaborative effort.

We knew from the outset that this work would face scepticism. The equine world is entrenched in tradition. We have grown up accepting that there are grumpy horses and that there are naughty horses. Our long-term goals were to change these misconceptions, to demonstrate that many of the behaviours which have been accepted as normal are actually abnormal and reflect discomfort. We need to reset what is regarded as normal. We had a mountain to climb, but we were determined to reach the summit and change peoples' perceptions and open their eyes to look and see and think.

YOU CAN MAKE A DIFFERENCE

What follows is our attempt to put the Ridden Horse Pain Ethogram in words and pictures that will help you to understand it and enable you to use it with your own horse. Many individuals and organisations have taken the time to give their thoughts on the subjects of equine welfare and the links between pain, performance and behaviour. To further improve the quality of life of horses, a team approach is essential. We share with you some of the latest research through 'Snippets of Science', and we are confident that you will find the ongoing research as encouraging as we do. Finally, we have gathered case studies where a change in behaviour was linked to musculoskeletal pain. Our aim is for these real-life examples to inspire you to make use of the information in this book, for the good of your horse.

We hope that some of our passion rubs off on you, and that some of your passion rubs off on your equestrian network. Between us all, we can make a difference. Please share this book, and the knowledge within it, with your friends. There are more projects in the pipeline, and exciting times on the horizon. Follow The Horse Physio on Facebook, Instagram, or through the blog and free newsletter at www.thehorsephysio.co.uk, for ongoing updates and more resources. Look out for courses, lectures, presentations, webinars and more from Dr Sue Dyson. Be part of the community that is working to make the world a better place for horses, one horse at a time. This community is using evidence-based practice and practice-based evidence, building knowledge and experience to ensure that all horses are happy athletes. We are proud to be leading this conversation, and we welcome you to our table.

CHAPTER 1

The Why: The Ridden Horse Pain Ethogram And The Right To Ride

"In riding a horse, we borrow freedom."
Helen Thompson

CASE STUDY: **STAR**
By Alice Clurow

"I went home, thinking I was failing her, thinking my instincts were way off, and decided to find a professional to help."

Star, a Dutch Warmblood x Trakehner chestnut filly, was born in June 2017, sharp and nervous. The first three years of Star's life were straightforward; she began to develop a sweet personality but was still sharp. Reluctant to back Star herself, Alice sent her to a professional yard. There, the mare was

Alice Clurow and Star

described as "one of the most difficult babies we've ever had to back".

Eight weeks later, Alice went to ride Star. "She was quiet and seemed subdued in comparison to the fiery little beast that I arrived with a couple of months previously," recalled Alice. "I took her for a hack, and she was the quietest three-year-old I had ever sat on. At the time, I thought they had done a fantastic job with her.

"I brought her home and lightly hacked her for a few weeks before turning her away for the winter to mature. She was quiet and easy to do at all times. She would happily lead the ride if we were in a group, and never spooked at anything. Amazing – or so I thought."

In February 2021, Alice brought Star in from her winter holiday and started groundwork, preparing to continue her education under saddle, and the four-year-old proved to be, once again, "the fiery little chestnut filly I knew and loved". However, after a couple of weeks of long-reining, lungeing and walking out with tack on, when Alice started to lean her weight over Star, the mare became sharp, reactive and opinionated.

"When she started pinning her ears when I was putting a saddle on, I decided she was trying to tell me something. Maybe I was going too fast? I went right back to basics and tried to make everything a positive experience – I set her up to succeed rather than to fail. We did baby steps with everything, but she only got worse. I spent hours by the mounting block trying to get her happy with me just being there. I could no longer lean over her without her pinning her ears, squealing, and kicking out. She started losing weight and muscle. It was time for the vet."

Star underwent back x-rays, a lameness work-up and blood tests. On the x-ray, four spinous processes appeared close together, with white marks around the top of these, which Alice queried. "The vet said it was nothing to be concerned about. The advice was to start from scratch and re-back Star."

Star received treatment from a physiotherapist and chiropractor, who were both satisfied with her condition. However, although Star seemed happy with general handling, as soon as Alice approached with the saddle, she saw pinned ears and worried eyes. "I didn't know how to proceed any slower with her. I was convinced something wasn't right."

Concerned Star was showing signs of kissing spines, Alice sought the opinion of a second vet. Kissing spines is the common term for impinging spinous processes, and many clinically normal horses have two or more impinging spinous processes. Often, horses are sedated for acquisition of back x-rays and therefore lower the head and neck, resulting in flexion of the back, potentially widening the spaces between the spinous processes. However, when ridden the back may be more extended, bringing the spinous processes closer together.

"The second vet had a look at the x-rays, checked Star's ovaries, did another lameness work-up, and scoped her stomach for ulcers. Once again, all was deemed well, and I was advised to re-back her again, reinforcing a positive experience. But I was so convinced that she was trying to tell me something and not just being naughty. There was just no reason for her to be so unhappy when she hadn't had any negative experiences. I went home, thinking I was failing her, thinking my instincts were way off, and decided to find a professional to help."

Alice contacted several local professionals who refused to help, being deterred by the extreme behaviour that Star had previously shown for no apparent reason. Eventually she found a lady based three hours' drive away who worked with many horses with behavioural problems. Alice discussed the history of Star, including the veterinary reports and the x-rays. After one week of working with Star the professional contacted Alice and said that she was concerned that the kissing spines may be the underlying cause of Star's behaviour.

With Alice's permission, local anaesthetic solution was infiltrated around the close spinous processes, and Alice rode Star, both before and afterwards. "I couldn't believe

Alice Clurow and Star

the difference. With the nerve block, I was able to walk, trot, and canter her in the school. She was wobbly and babyish, but relaxed, and it was obvious that pain was the issue all along. She had been trying to tell me something and although it took three vets to recognise the problem, we had got there and there was a glimmer of hope for us."

Star underwent surgery, a 'bone shave and a ligament snip', before returning home to recover and start rehabilitation. "After two weeks I noticed she was putting weight on, her coat became shiny, and she seemed much happier. Her eyes became full of wonder and inquisitiveness, rather than stress and worry. Looking back at that submissive three-year-old that came home after being backed, she had probably accepted the pain and switched herself off. The following year, I think she found her voice again and decided to communicate her feelings."

As part of her management plan Star has treatment from a physiotherapist every six weeks. "The most important thing for me is that I now have a happy, loving, relaxed mare who is physically strong and trusts me to let her know things are okay. She wants to please. Every so often the pain memory creeps in, and we find ourselves in a bit of a muddle, but overall, she is happy and pain free." It is possible, indeed likely, that the behaviour that is perceived as 'pain memory' may result from an additional intermittent source of discomfort.

"We have created the most wonderful bond and I know now to always trust my gut with her. If something doesn't feel right, it probably isn't."

LET'S START WITH SOME QUESTIONS:

1. What is meant by the term equestrianism's social license?
2. How can you tell if your horse is 'happy'?
3. How can you tell if your horse is 'unhappy'?
4. What classes as an equine welfare concern?
5. What can be done to improve equine welfare?

EQUESTRIANISM'S SOCIAL LICENSE TO OPERATE

Why do you need to understand about equestrianism's social license to operate?

You have probably come across the phrase 'social licence' in relation to equestrianism. It's become a buzz phrase over the past year or two. But what does it mean, and how does it apply to you and your horse?

In May 2022, World Horse Welfare commissioned a survey of over two thousand adults, representative of the United Kingdom population in terms of gender and socio-economic background

Some of the key findings were:

- *Two in five (40%) people only supported the continued involvement of horses in sport if their welfare is improved. Three in five (60%) said there should be more safety and welfare measures in place in horse sports.*
- *16% felt that media coverage over the past couple of years had negatively impacted their confidence in protection of horse welfare in sport.*
- *One in five (20%) did not support the continued involvement of horses in sport in any circumstances.*

Similar results were acquired later in 2022 from surveys involving both the lay public (14,273) and equestrian enthusiasts (27,710) from 14 countries. These surveys were organised by the Equine Ethics and Wellbeing Commission, an

A comfortable Grand Prix dressage horse in extended trot

independent committee appointed by the Fédération Equestre Internationale (FEI).

What we see on the outside can be very different from what we feel on the inside. As a horse owner and rider, you know how much you love your horse, and you do your best in terms of his or her well-being and quality of life. Mistakes are sometimes made through lack of knowledge, not through deliberate malpractice. If you want horse riding to be something that your children and grandchildren can enjoy, we all need to 'up our game' in terms of equine welfare and it is important that non-equestrians recognise these efforts.

There are voices from inside and outside the world of equestrianism who are questioning the ethics of owning and riding horses and questioning the welfare of ridden horses. Without public recognition that we are putting horses first, the sport of riding horses is at risk, both for competition and for leisure.

What is a 'social license'?

The social licence to operate is an unwritten, non-legally binding contract whereby society 'gives' the right to operate. Basically, it's whether the public are okay with something. It's a concept that originated in resource-based industries, but more recently has been applied to animal-based industries. If public perception is against a specific concept (for example, riding or competing horses), then pressure from the public can cause that concept to be changed, or even stopped completely from operating. When a group has social licence to operate, it's able to continue with minimal formalised restrictions. Without the social licence to operate, the activity may be outlawed or curtailed, even if it's still legal.

An example of this is the use of wild animals in the circus. For example, can you remember the elephant that was chained on the village green each year with the touring circus? Today, most of us would recognise this as detrimental to the elephant, and definitely not in its best interest. The loss of social licence to operate has already led to the banning of greyhound racing in Canberra in Australia, and in many states in the USA, and to the banning of horse racing over jumps in most of Australia.

A horse show jumping with good technique

Why is equestrianism's social license at risk?

The equine industry is at a potential turning point, with increased discussion about the social licence to compete. The welfare of horses engaged in equestrian sport is currently in the spotlight. Awareness and interest are greatly increased, particularly after events such as the Tokyo Olympics and the subsequent dropping of riding from the Olympic modern pentathlon; the debate about three or four in an Olympic team, in particular for showjumping and eventing; the recent unsuccessful litigation by People for the Ethical Treatment of Animals (PETA) against the Dutch dressage rider Edward Gal for excessive use of rollkur; the Fédération Equestre Internationale's (FEI) suspension of Brazilian dressage rider, Leandro Aparecido Da Silva, for abusing his daughter's pony; the FEI's suspension of American show jumper

Andy Kocher for the use of electric spurs; the rapping allegations against the German show jumper Ludger Beerbaum; and the temporary suspension of Sir Mark Todd, former world-class event rider, by the British Horse Racing Authority, for beating a horse during a cross-country training session. The book 'I Can't Watch Anymore' was published in 2022 (Taylor, J. 'I can't watch anymore': The case for dropping equestrian from the Olympic Games. Epona Media, Copenhagen, Denmark, 2022). This book argues that all equestrian sports should be removed from the Olympic Games. The French Parliament have made sweeping recommendations for changes of riding and management practices ahead of the Paris 2024 Olympic Games. There has never been a greater need for the equine industry to act proactively to protect the future of equestrian sports.

What can you do to help?

To maintain our social licence, we must be ethical, accountable, and transparent. We need to be willing to recognise when things could be better, to admit when things need to change, and to act upon this knowledge. What horse riders see as ethical may be different to what the non-equestrian public see as ethical. What we saw as ethical ten years ago may be different to what we see as ethical today. With the internet and social media as they are, it's easy for the less pleasant aspects of horsemanship and the equestrian world to be shared globally in just minutes. As always, bad news sells. The mistreatment of animals is an emotive subject, and the public will judge our sport on how we treat our horses. We can and must be proactive in promoting the use of horses in sports and leisure activities as a mutually beneficial experience, with the welfare of the horse at the heart of it all, to maintain the reputation and future of equestrian sports.

Welfare includes both physical and mental well-being. Just because something has always been done a particular way does not mean that is the way it should be done. A favourite phrase is 'If you always do what you always did, you'll always get what you always got'. It is high time that as a community, we re-evaluate how we ride and manage horses, particularly in terms of recognising the links between pain, performance and behaviour. Horse ownership comes with a responsibility to keep your knowledge up to date. Following and acting on emerging evidence can give you the confidence that you are doing the best you can for your horse, given the knowledge, tools and experience that you have available to you right now.

Improved welfare leads to improved performance

Maintaining and improving the welfare of horses is not only the right thing to do, but it also leads to better results. The charity World Horse Welfare is funding a study to develop an ethical framework for equestrian sport. This study is ongoing, but initial trials across several disciplines suggest that this framework is helpful in making decisions on an ethical basis. The links between improved welfare and improved performance are a great example of a win-win situation.

To improve horse welfare, we need to apply the knowledge that we already have, and to invest in more research to further develop this knowledge. We must evaluate new information and be open to change. Rules and regulations within equestrianism should consider the current science and should be applied to routine horse care as well as to horse sports. Monitoring adherence to these rules and regulations will not be easy, but each of us has a responsibility not only to our own horse, but also to equestrian sport as a whole.

What is good welfare?

So, what is good welfare? This applies not only to ridden horses, but to horse care and management in general. The United Kingdom Animal Welfare Act 2006 states:

1. *A person commits an offence if he does not take such steps as are reasonable in all the circumstances to ensure that the needs of an animal for which he is responsible are met to the extent required by good practice*
2. *For the purposes of this Act, an animal's needs shall be taken to include—*
   (a) its need for a suitable environment,
   (b) its need for a suitable diet,
   (c) its need to be able to exhibit normal behaviour patterns,
   (d) any need it has to be housed with, or apart from, other animals, and
   (e) its need to be protected from pain, suffering, injury and disease.

3. *The circumstances to which it is relevant to have regard when applying subsection (1) include, in particular—*
   (a) any lawful purpose for which the animal is kept, and
   (b) any lawful activity undertaken in relation to the animal."

In the majority of countries in the developed world there is legislation that is as stringent as that of the United Kingdom, if not more so.

You have probably heard of the five freedoms, which cover an animal's diet, environment, health, behavioural interactions and mental state. The Animal Welfare Act 2006 looks at minimising the negative aspects of these. In reality, as horse riders we need to go further than this, and to provide our horses with positive experiences, as well as avoiding negative ones. We enjoyed a phrase from Roly Owers, Chief Executive of the charity World Horse Welfare, who said in his presentation at the Saddle Research Trust International Conference in December 2021 that we should provide 'friends, freedom and forage'. One difficulty can be in agreeing what constitutes a positive experience. We have so much knowledge at our fingertips, but it is tricky to know what is valid and helpful, and what we would be better to ignore.

Is your horse being naughty?

Traditionally, if a ridden horse is resisting what is being asked it is labelled as 'naughty' and often punished. The phrase 'punitive training techniques' basically means training the horse by telling him off, by punishing him when he does what we deem to be 'wrong'. This is contrary to the accepted principles of learning theory. As human beings, it can be hard to accept that we need to change our behaviour, and it's even harder to actually create that change and maintain it. We now have solid evidence linking certain ridden behaviours to musculoskeletal pain, in a format that can be used by all horse riders. We are sharing these behaviours with you in this book, alongside some of the studies providing evidence connecting pain and behaviour in ridden horses. As horse riders, we need to recognise what behaviours can be pain related, and we need to understand how to use that information. This requires sharing of knowledge and clarity of communication. Once you recognise the links between pain and behaviour, it is no longer okay to punish a horse for demonstrating behaviours that are proven to be linked to pain.

A horse performing well cross country at Badminton three-day event

Treat your horse with respect, compassion and understanding

Good welfare focuses on both the physical and the mental well-being of a horse. Responding appropriately to a horse's communication is important for mental well-being, as well as physical health. Imagine how you would feel if you were trying to tell your trainer that you were finding something difficult because you were hurting, and they just shouted at you more loudly, or worse, hit you to make you keep trying.

We are not saying that anyone has got it all sorted, or that anyone knows how to get it right all the time. There is always more to learn, and all of us could get better at listening and understanding. What we are saying is that you must continue to do your best, and that you must make use of up-to-date knowledge and experience, using qualified, trusted team members and mentors to guide you in being your horse's caregiver and partner.

A vision we wholeheartedly embrace is that of World Horse Welfare, "A world where every horse is treated with respect, compassion and understanding". Each of us is responsible for our own education, and for putting into action what we learn. We owe it to our horses, to ourselves, and to equestrianism, to put the welfare of the horse as our top priority, and to show the world that this is the case.

The benefits of riding horses

Those of you who own and ride horses instinctively know that horse riding is good for you. There is undoubtedly plenty of science to support this, for both able-bodied and healthy individuals and those with physical or mental impediments. In this book, however, we discuss how riding horses can be good for your horse and share some of the evidence that supports this.

Riding horses is part of equestrian culture throughout the world. It is not the only way of being involved with horses, either for sport or for leisure, but it is probably the most common activity. As a rider who loves horses, it is easy to assume that the horse feels the same benefits as the rider, in terms of both physical and psychological health. Can you be certain that this is the case? How can you find out?

As someone who is striving to do better for their horse, you will know that there is always more to learn. The focus of science has tended to be on recognising negative aspects of equine welfare. More recently, researchers are delving into how to recognise positive aspects of the quality of life and well-being of horses. Good welfare is about promoting what is good, as well as minimising what is bad.

There will always be outliers, people who do extreme good, and people who do extreme bad. That is the case in the horse world, as in all other areas of life. In today's society, an example of 'bad' can be whipped up into a storm in no time at all; we focus more of our attention on the negative than we do on the positive. We are horrified at the stories of abuse that make the news. The actions of a few are shared far and wide. The reality, of course, is that most of you would be devastated to think that you were causing your horse harm. We proactively promote horse riding and the use of horses in competitive sports, but we also realise that we have to be cognisant of evidence-based robust research. Not all published research is robust, nor evidence-based. Some may be biased. Poor science sometimes gets perpetuated through incorrect citations. We endeavour to promote research which we have critically analysed and believe is factually based, while recognising that it is virtually impossible to perform perfect scientific studies in the field. The research about the Ridden Horse Pain Ethogram (RHpE), also known as the performance check list, has flaws, but we believe that these have been openly acknowledged and the cumulative body of evidence now published indicates the value of the RHpE as a valuable tool for everyone involved with equestrianism in all its guises.

Is your horse 'happy'?

As your horse's carer, it is up to you to do your best for the horse. You must do what you can to keep up to date with the current knowledge and build a team of experts around your horse that you can lean on and learn from. If you look back, it is likely that there are things you would have done differently, if you had known then what you now know. We most certainly feel this way! If you are lucky enough to look back in twenty years, it is likely that you will feel much the same way then about what you are currently doing. This applies to many areas of life, not just to horse care and management. It is not good enough to blindly follow in the steps of tradition. It can be hard to forge a new path, but as Albert Einstein said, "The measure of intelligence is the ability to change".

The FEI Dressage Rules 2022 state that 'The object of dressage is the development of the horse into a happy athlete…' (Chapter 1, Dressage, Article 401, Object and General Principles of Dressage). 'Happy' is an anthropomorphic term which perhaps we should not be using. What is an 'happy athlete'? And how do we know if an equine athlete is not 'happy'? It is hard to define a 'happy horse', but it is very likely that pain and discomfort will lead to an 'unhappy horse'. It therefore follows that the ability to recognise pain or discomfort at an early stage will give horses a better quality of life and will lead to improved welfare.

How do you know if your horse is in pain?

Are you confident that you can recognise when your horse is in pain? Roly Owers, Chief Executive of World Horse Welfare, asked this question of the audience at the beginning of a webinar in 2020. His guest speaker was Dr

Sue Dyson, a world-renowned expert in equine orthopaedics with a specialist interest in lameness and poor performance in sports horses, and co-author of this book.

The answer to Roly's question was that around a quarter of the audience felt they would find it difficult to recognise pain behaviour. Our experience is that it is far more difficult to recognise pain behaviour than many people believe. This is in part because historically horses were prey animals, and it was important for their survival to conceal signs of pain. There also is a lack of understanding of what a normal healthy horse looks like. We have tried to provide images of normal horses to contrast with those showing behavioural signs likely reflecting pain. Our experiences as professionals within the world of equestrianism reinforce the need for better recognition of pain related behaviour in ridden horses. As mentioned in the Preface of this book, Dr Sue Dyson found herself so frustrated by the difficulties of recognising pain in horses that she set about developing a way to measure pain behaviour in ridden horses. So was born the RHpE, the performance check list.

The Ridden Horse Pain Ethogram

In this book, we are going to take you on a tour of the RHpE (the performance check list), and how you can apply it to your horse. Reading, digesting, using, and sharing the information contained within this book will help you to understand how you can use the RHpE (the performance check list) to improve performance, and to monitor your horse's level of comfort in his/her ridden work. It's important that we, as equestrians, become better at recognising pain. Only once we have recognised pain can we investigate it and treat it. As Dr Dyson says, "Problems which are labelled as training related, rider related, behavioural, or 'that's just how the horse has always gone', are usually pain related". Through recognising, investigating and treating pain, we will improve the welfare and performance of horses. To maintain the social licence to operate that equestrians currently enjoy, we must learn more about what makes horses 'happy', and we must act on this knowledge.

TALKING POINTS

1. *Looking at it from your horse's point of view, what are three things you could do to improve his/her happiness?*
2. *Looking at it from the point of view of the general public, what are three things that the equestrian world could do to improve equine welfare?*
3. *Do we choose to believe our horses are 'happy' because we can't bear the thought that they might not be happy?*

CASE STUDY: **DEVINE**
By Kathy

"She was very sweet and personable on the ground, but under saddle she turned into a cranky, hard ride."

Devine

Devine came to Kathy to be sold after a period of time off and had no known pre-existing lameness problems. Confident the sale would be simple, Kathy began easing the mare back into work to develop her base fitness. However, as Devine became fitter and her workload increased, Kathy started to notice some odd behaviours under saddle that did not improve with training.

"She would move her head up and down a lot, and either curl her chin to her chest or stick her head straight down to the ground," explained Kathy. "She also had a very slow-tempo trot and canter that for the life of me I couldn't get to be quicker. We did all the normal stuff – checked her teeth and her saddle – but she still seemed uncomfortable. She was very sweet and personable on the ground, but under saddle she turned into a cranky, hard ride."

Kathy took Devine to the yard of a friend, who had just completed Sue Dyson's online course about the RHpE and showed Kathy pictures of ways in which horses can display pain under saddle. Kathy asked her friend to score Devine using the RHpE, and they came up with a score of 12 out of 24, strongly indicating that Devine was in pain. "I felt terrible. Even though Devine wasn't limping, I understood from the RHpE that she was in pain somewhere."

Devine underwent a full lameness work-up and was found to have 'negative plantar angles' in both hind feet, meaning that the lower border of the distal phalanges (pedal bones) sloped downwards from front to back. In addition, both hind pastern joints were subluxated – not in correct alignment – and she had severe arthritis in one hock.

Her hocks were injected, and Devine also underwent a significant trimming and shoeing change, before progressively resuming work. "The difference has been remarkable. She's happy to go forward, she's not spooky, she holds her head steady into the contact. All the problems I was trying to address with more training, more hours in the saddle, another cavalletti exercise, or a lesson with a new trainer went away once the horse was pain free.

"Now, all my sales horses get evaluated using the RHpE. Some owners take some convincing, but most are happy to get to the root of their horses' difficulties. We sell fewer horses now because some lameness issues cannot be quickly resolved. However, I feel much better about the horses I am selling because I know they are as comfortable as possible."

SNIPPETS OF SCIENCE

"…situations where human–animal interactions may have positive welfare impacts include: when the companionable presence of humans provides company and feelings of safety, when humans provide preferred foods, tactile contacts and/or training reinforcements, when humans participate in enjoyable routine activities or in engaging variable activities, when the presence of familiar humans is calming in threatening circumstances and when humans act to end periods of deprivation, inhibition or harm."

Mellor, D., Beausoleil, N., Littlewood, K., McLean, A., McGreevy, P., Jones, B., Wilkins, C. The 2020 five domains model: Including human–animal interactions in assessments of animal welfare. Animals 2020, 10: 1870. https://doi:10.3390/ani10101870

"To identify the main concerns and discuss the potential to improve the welfare of these equine athletes, a workshop involving participants from equestrian sports and animal welfare research was held. Participants concluded that the main challenges in equine welfare arise from conflicts between competition demands and the basic needs of the horse."

Furtado, T., Preshaw, L., Hockenhull, J., Wathan, J., Douglas, J., Horseman, S., Smith, R., Pollard, D., Pinchbeck, G., Rogers, J., Hall, C. How happy are equine athletes? Stakeholder perceptions of equine welfare issues associated with equestrian sport. Animals 2021, 11: 3228. https://doi.org/10.3390/ani11113228

"A person commits an offence if he does not take such steps as are reasonable in all the circumstances to ensure that the needs of an animal for which he is responsible are met to the extent required by good practice."

Animal Welfare Act 2006, https://www.legislation.gov.uk/ukpga/2006/45/contents

DR ROSIE JONES MCVEY

Dr Rosie Jones-McVey

Dr Rosie Jones McVey is a horse trainer, recommended trainer for Intelligent Horsemanship, and a social anthropologist. She conducted ethnographic fieldwork with British horse people for her PhD, based at Cambridge University, and is now engaged in a postdoctoral study of Equine Assisted Therapies

Dr Jones McVey discusses 'contingent characters'

"Empathy is often described as the capacity to put yourself in someone else's shoes. This means that you can understand the suffering of another person, and so, be motivated to help. But of course, for it to be of any use to that suffering person at all, it is important that we don't just imagine ourselves in their shoes – and join them in their woe. We have to imagine a different role for ourselves, as the one who can provide some sort of solution. To be a helpful empathiser, we don't just need to equivocate ourselves with others, we need to recognise our capacity to be something important to them – an advocate, helper, supporter, protector, or whatever else.

In order to understand our roles in relation to one another, people use stories. These are not always the sorts of elaborate, formalised, stories that are written in books or told by the fireside. They are also fleeting, subconscious meaning-making mechanisms. When a man comes into a bank wearing a balaclava and carrying a swag sack, we can easily make sense of how to read his character and what it means to us – we quickly and subconsciously put him into a story and can tell the sort of thing that is going on. Characters in stories relate to one another. I call this, 'contingent characters' because they can't make sense without one another. So, for example, Romeo needs Juliet to make sense. Or, when I think of my children, I evaluate myself as a mother, but when I think of my studies, I understand myself quite differently.

What does this have to do with our relationship with horses?

When we think about our horse's character, we are always, subconsciously, at the same time, thinking about who we are in relation to that. If we describe the horse as 'crazy', we might well be thinking about ourselves as brave or resilient in handling him. If we describe the horse as childlike, we are probably emphasising our responsibility towards him as maternal/paternal. This means, in order to allow ourselves to recognise that a horse is in pain, we need to be ready to recognise what that would mean for who we would need to be. (Authors' comment: This means that the rider, having recognised that their horse is in pain, may need to change their mindset, for example to alter their aspirations for the horse.) During my ethnographic fieldwork among British horse riders, I noticed horse owners would interpret similar veterinary advice very differently. Sometimes, riders failed to acknowledge there could be pain in their horse, because they were not ready to acknowledge who they would have to become if this were the case – a carer, perhaps, rather than a competitive partner.

It is a good idea to check in with yourself – what stakes do you have invested in the idea that your horse is pain free? Or, in contrast, what stakes do you have invested in the idea that your horse is in pain? Perhaps it is easier to recognise yourself as somebody who can provide physical care than somebody who can handle behavioural issues? Most people tend to be happier, if honest with themselves, with one or other story, while of course, in most cases, it is rarely a simple case of behaviour OR pain.

This is not just a new way to talk about 'projection'. Because, with the term 'projection' the suggestion is that we can somehow cleanse ourselves of that and look at the horse completely 'neutrally'. It can't be done. If we are going to ethically relate to them at all, we are going to invest in the way our characters relate to one another in meaningful plots. The trick, then, is not coming at this with no investment, but checking in that we can be flexible in accepting a different story if the need arises, and not becoming stuck in identifying our horses in line with our own comfortable corresponding identity."

DR LYNDA BIRKE

Dr Lynda Birke and Dalusha

Dr Lynda Birke was Senior Lecturer in Women and Gender Studies at the University of Warwick, U.K. Her PhD is in biology, specialising in animal behaviour, in which she did research for many years. She has a particular interest in animal welfare and ethics and has served on several ethical and welfare committees. Since taking early retirement, she has concentrated on research in animal welfare and human/animal relationships and is currently an Associate Editor for Society and Animals.

In response to our question, 'How is horse riding good for the horse as well as the rider?', Dr Birke replied:

For the horse, riding can provide enrichment. There are mental challenges which the horse can meet, which are especially important for horses who are stabled, but even pastured horses don't exactly have a varied environment. Whether going out for a hack or going to a competition or fun ride, there are many different stimuli. True, that can lead to overstimulation – so it matters that humans are sensitive to this.

Movement: although horses at pasture are moving much of the time, their range of movement might be quite limited. Riding can provide a greater range of movement, which is likely to be beneficial – not only for musculoskeletal function, but also for horses' minds. I'm reminded of a paper Ann Game wrote a few years ago. She talked about her horse becoming ill and getting paralysed. Even after initial recovery, the mare was unable to canter properly. The trainer told Ann to ride – which (with trepidation!) she did. Her own bodily movements, learned long ago, were felt by the horse, who was then able to canter. To start with, she could do it only with Ann's bodily help. The same applies to humans benefitting from riding horses.....

Communication and companionship: riding is always an act of communication, creating companionship between species. For stabled horses, that matters especially. But all horses can benefit from creating that. Horses have come to recognise, over millennia of domestication, human intentions, and can "read" our emotions. I have no doubt that they can do that through riding as much as they can when face to face with us. The act of riding thus enables a fine-tuning of those communication skills. Same for people – it reminds us that horses are not vehicles: they are thinking, sentient, beings. Always good to remember that!

CHAPTER 2

The What: Developing The Ridden Horse Pain Ethogram

"The horse, with beauty unsurpassed, strength immeasurable and grace unlike any other, still remains humble enough to carry a man upon his back."

Amber Senti

CASE STUDY: **BRIO**
By Hannah
Knaebel-Seierstad

"Even though I had been doing everything in my power to help her, I felt I was still failing to be the horse owner I wanted to be."

Hannah bought Brio, a well-bred Connemara cross with high expectations to be her forever horse, to fulfil dreams of galloping cross-country, fun clinics with friends, and trail rides

Brio

through the woods. However, as Brio's workload increased, she struggled to perform.

"I did everything I could think of to address her resistance: time off, a new saddle, dental evaluations, ulcer treatments, hormone treatments, supplements, groundwork, chiropractic and acupuncture treatment, more time off and another new saddle", said Hannah. "She was never 'lame', and the resistance looked more like training or behavioural issues. Professionals told me it was normal young horse behaviour." However, there are some common misconceptions amongst horse people about what may be normal responses for a young horse to training. There should be progressive improvement if training methods are correct, and the horse is pain-free.

"In the barn, Brio was sweet and affectionate. She excelled at in-hand work and learned quickly. But she was entirely different under saddle: distracted and spooky, inconsistent in the bridle, hard to get forward and even harder to keep on the correct canter lead. The horse I had on the ground was very different from the horse I rode, and that bothered me."

It was watching the Equitopia webinar series on Sue Dyson's RHpE and the associated research that sharpened Hannah's vision of what might be behind Brio's behaviour, but the realisation also brought with it a level of guilt. "I could see my horse, her behaviour, and her expressions through clearer and cleaner eyes.

"Even though I had been doing everything in my power to help Brio, I felt I was still failing to be the horse owner I wanted to be. I was hearing two conflicting viewpoints. Firstly, that of the professionals who put the 'blame' of Brio's behaviour on her, or my riding skills. The other viewpoint was from Dr Dyson; that the behaviour was no one's fault, but an expression of pain. Of the two opinions, it was Dr Dyson's that had supportive data that was fact-checked.

"There was no more guilt or shame over my skill or her personality. I was going to find the facts that would be unmoved by personal or professional opinion. I could get off the hamster wheel of bouncing from trainer to vet to chiropractor. I was going to find facts, face them realistically, and pursue a solution."

Hannah asked a friend to video her riding Brio doing the movements that Dr Dyson recommends for application of the RHpE, including trotting 10-metre diameter circles in each direction, transitions, and cantering 20-metre diameter circles in each direction. "I watched the video carefully, slowing it down as needed so that I could watch the facial expressions and counting the number of seconds a particular behaviour occurred, and concluded that the RHpE score was 12 out of 24.

"When I watched the video, not through training eyes, but via the lens of the RHpE, I felt both happy and sad. I was relieved that our struggles could finally be resolved, but I was disappointed that I hadn't found Dr Dyson's work sooner. I was certain that this was the beginning of real change for both Brio and me.

"I knew it would take some work to convince my vet to do a lameness evaluation on a horse that wasn't 'lame'. I showed her Dr Dyson's research and we talked about the RHpE." Hannah's vet assessed Brio in hand, after flexion tests and on the lunge. No lameness was seen in hand and Brio's movement did not change after flexion tests, but she reacted to the hindlimbs being flexed by pinning her ears – not normal for a pain-free horse. Although she appeared sound on the lunge, Brio was reluctant to go forward, pinning her ears, swishing her tail and kicking out.

Hannah then rode Brio for the vet, including circles in trot and canter and transitions. The vet applied the RHpE, agreed the horse was uncomfortable, and then opted to x-ray Brio's hocks and stifles and to acquire ultrasonographic images of the stifles.

In the left stifle there was an increased amount of fluid, indicative of inflammation, and evidence of injury of the distal end of the medial patellar ligament. The right stifle also had increased joint fluid. There was a hypoechoic lesion in the middle patellar ligament, evidence of additional injury at the distal end of the medial patellar ligament, a roughened edge of the medial meniscus close to the medial collateral ligament, and bony proliferation on the medial side of the joint reflecting osteoarthritis. The pain was bilateral, so Brio had never presented as overtly lame on one hindlimb because both hindlimbs hurt.

The stifles were 'blocked' by injection of local anaesthetic solution, and the flexion, lunge and ridden tests were repeated, with clear improvement. "The biggest revelation was what I felt when I rode her. With her stifles pain-free, I had an entirely different horse. Brio was forward, happy and attentive. She was steady in the bridle, light off my leg, consistent in a soft uphill frame. Everything I had been struggling with was gone; the resistance, the spooking, the inconsistencies – all gone. She was the horse I knew she had the potential to be. I pulled up to a halt, looked at the vet, and both of us were in tears. A massive weight had lifted off my shoulders. We finally had answers."

Brio underwent arthroscopic surgery to examine and debride the damaged cartilage and remove bone chips. She then began a lengthy rehabilitation process with shockwave therapy, PRP (platelet rich plasma), and Adequan[R] (polysulphated glycosaminoglycan).

Hannah Knaebel-Seierstad and Flynn

"Brio has continued to make good progress and is gaining strength. She will probably never be my performance horse, but I'm fine with that. The 10 minutes I had with her totally pain-free will be the most influential 10 minutes of my riding career. Never again will I blame the horse's personality or my skill for behaviours I know from the RHpE are because of pain. The RHpE saved me from years of self-doubt, and Brio from untold pain and frustration. It's now a regular part of my riding and training programme.

"While I am sad that I don't get the fun of cross-country jumping or collecting ribbons, Brio has given me something of the most enormous value, which is knowledge. She took me from frustration to clarity. To feel the difference of a pain-free horse means more than any show. Every horse and rider deserve to experience the feeling Brio and I had for those wonderful 10 minutes; happy, connected, and moving with ease."

LET'S START WITH SOME QUESTIONS:

1. *What is pain?*
2. *Why do we need to know if a horse is in pain?*
3. *How can you tell if your horse is in pain when you are riding?*
4. *What is 'lameness'?*
5. *What might affect your ability to detect pain in your horse during ridden work?*

INTRODUCING THE RIDDEN HORSE PAIN ETHOGRAM

What is the Ridden Horse Pain Ethogram?

The Ridden Horse Pain Ethogram (RHpE) is a list of 24 behaviours, each with strict definitions, that might be seen in a ridden horse. Studies have shown that if a horse displays eight or more of these 24 behaviours, then the horse is likely to have pain or discomfort. It is important to recognise that although there may be a variety of reasons for each of the 24 behaviours, in the context of the RHpE (performance check list) it is the total number of behaviours which is the crux.

A horse can only communicate pain or discomfort through its behaviour or performance. If a horse has been in discomfort ever since you have known it, then you might not see any changes in that behaviour or performance. This doesn't mean the problem is not pain related, it simply means that the pain has been there since you first met that horse. We hope that one day, to overcome on-going performance and behaviour problems, riders, trainers, coaches and all other equestrian professionals will first look for physical problems in a horse, rather than trying to fix the performance problems initially by training the horse or the rider. Only once pain and discomfort have been ruled out, with the RHpE as one of the tools used to do this, should the problem be dealt with through training.

Journal of Veterinary Behavior 23 (2018) 47–57

Contents lists available at ScienceDirect

Journal of Veterinary Behavior

journal homepage: www.journalvetbehavior.com

Research

Development of an ethogram for a pain scoring system in ridden horses and its application to determine the presence of musculoskeletal pain

CrossMark

Sue Dyson [a,*], Jeannine Berger [b], Andrea D. Ellis [c], Jessica Mullard [a]

[a] Centre for Equine Studies, Animal Health Trust, Lanwades Park, Newmarket, Suffolk, United Kingdom
[b] San Francisco SPCA, San Francisco, California
[c] Unequi Ltd., West Bridgford, Nottinghamshire, United Kingdom

ARTICLE INFO

Article history:
Received 29 August 2017
Received in revised form
17 October 2017
Accepted 21 October 2017
Available online 1 November 2017

Keywords:
Lameness
Equine behavior
Pain grading
Headshaking
Bucking
Rearing

ABSTRACT

There is evidence that more than 47% of the sports horse population in normal work may be lame, but the lameness is not recognized by owners or trainers. An alternative means of detecting pain may be recognition of behavioral changes in ridden horses. It has been demonstrated that there are differences in facial expressions in nonlame and lame horses. The purpose of this study was to develop a whole horse ethogram for ridden horses and to determine whether it could be applied repeatedly by 1 observer (repeatability study, 9 horses) and if, by application of a related pain behavior score, lame horses (n = 24) and nonlame horses (n = 13) could be differentiated. It was hypothesized that there would be some overlap in pain behavior scores among nonlame and lame horses; and that overall, nonlame horses would have a lower pain behavior score than lame horses. The ethogram was developed with 117 behavioral markers, and the horses were graded twice in random order by a trained specialist using video footage. Overall, there was a good correlation between the 2 assessments ($P < 0.001$; $R^2 = 0.91$). Behavioral markers that were not consistent across the 2 assessments were omitted, reducing the ethogram to 70 markers. The modified ethogram was applied to video recordings of the nonlame horses and lame horses (ethogram evaluation). There was a strong correlation between 20 behavioral markers and the presence of lameness. The ethogram was subsequently simplified to 24 behavioral markers, by the amalgamation of similar behaviors which scored similarly and by omission of markers which showed unreliable results in relation to lameness. Following this, the maximum individual occurrence score for lame horses was 14 (out of 24 possible markers), with a median and mean score of 9 (± 2 standard deviation) compared with a maximum score of 6 for nonlame horses, with a median and mean score of 2 (± 1.4). For lame horses, the following behaviors occurred significantly more ($P < 0.05$, chi-square): ears back, mouth opening, tongue out, change in eye posture and expression, going above the bit, head tossing, tilting the head, unwillingness to go, crookedness, hurrying, changing gait spontaneously, poor quality canter, resisting, and stumbling and toe dragging. Recognition of these features as potential indicators of musculoskeletal pain may enable earlier recognition of lameness and avoidance of punishment-based training. Further research is necessary to verify this new ethogram for assessment of pain in ridden horses.

What are 'pain' and 'discomfort'?

A horse exhibiting signs likely to reflect discomfort: an intense stare, the right ear is back, the head is tilted with the nose to the left, the nostrils are flared and the horse is sweating profusely.

We would like to take a moment to define 'pain' and 'discomfort'. The Oxford Advanced Learners Dictionary defines pain as "the feelings that you have in your body when you have been hurt or when you are ill". The Cambridge English Dictionary defines it as "a feeling of physical suffering caused by injury or illness". The International Association for the Study of Pain describes pain as "An unpleasant sensory and emotional experience associated with, or resembling that associated with, actual or potential tissue damage".

The word 'discomfort' is defined in the Oxford Advanced Learners Dictionary as "a feeling of slight pain or of being physically uncomfortable". In our work with horses, we find that many people are happier to think and talk about 'discomfort' in horses, rather than 'pain'. Based on the above definition, we can see that discomfort is simply a milder version of pain. Therefore, from this point on, for ease of reading, we will refer to 'pain' as meaning 'pain and discomfort'.

Why was the RHpE developed?

Back to the Ridden Horse Pain Ethogram. We mentioned earlier that a horse which is in pain is likely to show eight or more of the 24 behaviours that comprise the RHpE. It is also possible that a horse in pain can show less than eight of the 24 behaviours. Individual horses react to pain in different ways; therefore it is not possible to determine the source of the pain from the behaviours that are shown. In fact, a study has demonstrated that changing the rider can lead to a horse showing different behaviours, although if the horse is in pain, the number of behaviours shown is still likely to result in a RHpE score of at least 8/24. It is important to recognise that different horses have variable temperaments, pain thresholds and athletic ability, all features that may influence the RHpE score.

"But my horse isn't lame..."

Research has shown that horse owners and riders are not good at recognising lameness. Lameness is usually due to pain; therefore unrecognised lameness is a potential welfare problem. Not only that, but the longer that a horse has been lame, even if the lameness is only mild, usually the more difficult it is to resolve the problem. This is because a horse (or human, for that matter) which is in pain over a long period of time will develop compensations in the way that they move. These compensations can change muscle development and can in themselves create further problems and more pain. Anyone who has walked with a limp for a while, or who has had to use only one arm because the other is injured, for example, will understand this.

In the horse world, the tendency is to blame ridden problems on the rider, or on the horse's behaviour. The rider needs to be stronger, or tougher, or less crooked... or the horse is being 'naughty', or 'difficult', or 'awkward'. What if the truth is that the horse that is 'misbehaving' is actually sore or in pain? What if the only way the horse can communicate this is through his performance or his behaviour? Maybe the saddle doesn't fit as well as it could, or the horse needs dental treatment, or he's lame at a level that's too mild to be easily seen? Many veterinarians have little awareness of the links between pain and behaviour and receive little training on the identification of low-level lameness or the assessment of ridden horses.

A horse stopping at a drop fence into water

Unless the problem is recognised as pain behaviour, it is unlikely that the source of pain will be found, even with advanced diagnostic tools such as bone scans (nuclear scintigraphy). So-called 'hot spots' do not necessarily equate with pain. Unless the source of pain is found, it is hard to be confident that it is pain causing the problems during ridden exercise. This means that even if you take your 'misbehaving' horse to a veterinarian for a lameness work-up, the problem might still be labelled as behavioural. A tool such as the RHpE, to help both professionals and lay people to recognise pain in ridden horses, is invaluable.

What is 'lameness'?

Which brings us to what is 'lameness'? Lameness is defined in the Oxford Learners Dictionary as "The condition of being unable to walk well because of an injury to the leg or foot". In the Cambridge English Dictionary, lameness is defined as "The fact of being unable to walk correctly because of physical injury to or weakness in the legs or feet". In relation to horses, our choice of definition for the term 'lameness' is 'abnormal movement that changes when nerve blocks, regional anaesthesia or intra-articular anaesthesia remove the source of pain'. This applies not only to trot but to other movements and gaits as well.

That makes it sound way simpler than it actually is, of course! For example, if a horse is bilaterally lame (lame in both hindlimbs, or both forelimbs) then there might not any sign of limping or of asymmetry (differences between left and right sides). Some horses will keep going no matter what. Horses are prey animals and adopt many strategies to disguise pain. A 'high adrenaline' horse might be trying to mask pain. We discuss in a later chapter what you might hope to experience at a lameness work-up, and what diagnostic tests and treatment could be recommended. No matter what definition we use, the science is clear that, even at high-level competition, we are not great at knowing when a horse is lame, or when it is in pain. We hope that widespread use of the RHpE (a performance check list) will change that.

A lame horse before nerve blocks. The horse is refusing to go forwards, despite the rider's cues. There is a head tilt, the mouth is open and the tail is swishing.

The same horse after nerve blocks have abolished pain causing lameness. The horse is trotting freely forwards. The head is straight, the ears are forward, the mouth is closed and the tail is swinging.

Diagnosing lameness

On diagnosing lameness and on pain-related adaptations of gait, Dr Dyson says,

"If a horse is moderately lame on a single limb it is relatively straightforward to identify. Forelimb lameness is characterised by a head nod in rhythm with the two-beat trot, the head going down as the non-lame limb hits the ground. Hindlimb lameness is characterised by asymmetrical movement of the pelvis when viewed from behind. However, with mild lameness or lameness involving more than one limb, identification of lameness becomes more difficult because horses adapt their gaits in a variety of ways to minimise discomfort. With either forelimb

Palpation of an enlarged suspensory ligament

or hindlimb lameness, the horse will reduce the range of motion of the thoracolumbosacral region (i.e., it stiffens the back). The horse may shorten the step length. The height of arc of foot flight may be lower because of reduced push off and to lessen the impact forces generated through the limb when the foot lands. In a hindlimb, a lowered foot flight may result in a toe drag. Duty factor, the proportion of the stride time when any limb is bearing weight, may be increased so that a horse is able to share loads among limbs. When moving in a circle, a horse may adapt the way it orientates the head, neck and trunk, with increasing trunk lean and turning the head and neck to the outside to protect the lame limb(s). Overall, the trot may look less animated, and lack a suspension phase.

If a horse is lame on a single limb, then assigning a grade to the lameness is a good indicator of the level of discomfort experienced by the horse. However, if a horse is lame on more than one limb the pain in each limb may balance each other out, so paradoxically any lameness grade that is assigned may substantially underestimate the level of pain.

It has been suggested that the use of objective evaluation of lameness using inertial measurement units to quantify the degree of asymmetry is superior to subjective evaluation of gait. It certainly prevents bias when interpreting the response to nerve blocks. However, the current systems have limitations when assessing lameness associated with more than one limb, especially if the lameness is only detectable when a horse is ridden, which is a common scenario.

It is important to recognise that the absence of lameness in trot, either in hand, on the lunge or ridden, does not preclude the absence of pain which influences canter. In the two-beat trot the horse is sharing load between two *limbs, whereas in the three-beat canter, the canter is initiated by the trailing (outside) hindlimb, which bears weight alone. There are many modifications of canter which reflect musculoskeletal discomfort and are often an attempt to share load between limbs, or to reduce push-off or impact forces. These include close spatial and temporal placement of the hindlimbs (at its worst, so-called bunny hopping), being on the forehand, being 'earthbound', lack of hindlimb engagement and impulsion, becoming disunited, the canter lacking a suspension phase, a four-beat canter or abnormally wide placement of the hindlimbs with unusual elevation of the forehand."*

How was the RHpE developed?

The RHpE has been painstakingly developed, building on existing studies in humans as well as horses. Work on how to recognise pain in people's faces was extended to studies on how to recognise pain in the faces of horses. Initially, researchers looked at horses in the stable or the field, rather than when they were being ridden. In 2017, Dr Sue Dyson, Dr Jeannine Berger, Dr Jessica Mullard and Dr Andrea Ellis, supported by a grant from World Horse Welfare,

Dr Sue Dyson   *Dr Jeannine Berger*

Dr Andrea Ellis

Dr Jessica Mullard

published a preliminary investigation into the facial expressions of ridden horses. They showed that they could tell the difference between lame and non-lame horses through looking at the expressions on their faces in photographs.

Dr Dyson and her team moved on to studying video footage of non-lame and lame ridden horses. To begin with, they compiled an ethogram (list) of 117 behaviours seen in ridden horses, which included facial expressions, head position and movement, tail position and movements, body posture, and responses to the rider's cues. When they applied this ethogram to video footage of lame and non-lame horses, the list was narrowed down to 24 behaviours. The majority of these behaviours were at least ten times more likely to be seen in horses with musculoskeletal pain, compared with non-lame horses. This descriptive list of 24 behaviours is what is now known as the Ridden Horse Pain Ethogram (RHpE) or ridden horse performance check list.

Further investigation showed that horses which displayed eight or more of the 24 behaviours were likely to have musculoskeletal pain, although some lame horses had a RHpE score less than 8/24. In one of these studies, for example, the non-lame horses scored from 0 to 4/24, with the most common score being 2/24. The lame horses scored from 4 to 14/24, with the most common score being 9/24. The RHpE score went down in lame horses after the source(s) of pain was removed with nerve blocks. The researchers determined that the RHpE gave the same results, whether it was used by a trained assessor, or by untrained assessors from various equestrian professional backgrounds. There were some aspects of behaviour that the untrained assessors found more difficult to recognise, such as an intense stare, or the bit being pulled through to one side. Training and practice using the RHpE would help with this. The evidence that the RHpE score was lower after the lameness was resolved with nerve blocks, shows that there is a link (a causal relationship) between pain and behaviour. Historically it has been suggested that horses react to the memory of pain and are habituated in their behaviour. The rapid improvement in RHpE scores after removal of pain using nerve blocks makes it unlikely that there is a memory of musculoskeletal pain.

How has the RHpE been validated?

The RHpE was developed using video footage of ridden horses. Dr Dyson went on to study its use in real-time. A trained assessor used the RHpE to score horses from video footage and in real-time and showed that it worked well under both circumstances. Next a group of veterinarians evaluated 20 horse-rider combinations in real-time. The horses were in normal work and presumed sound by the owners, but assessment from an independent veterinarian revealed that some horses had low-grade lameness. Using just the RHpE the veterinarians were able to differentiate between horses with low-grade lameness and non-lame horses.

Video footage of those 20 horses was combined with a further 40 horses presumed sound by their owners, including riding school horses, and those used for general purpose (including unaffiliated competition), show jumping, eventing and dressage. The RHpE scores ranged from 3 to 16/24, with the most common score being 9/24. The researchers looked at the effect on the RHpE score of breed, sex, age, work discipline, back muscle spasm and soreness, poor saddle fit, rider skill, and the presence of lameness. Again, they found that a RHpE score of eight or more out of 24 was a good indicator of the presence of musculoskeletal pain.

Another study looked at horses in hand and ridden to assess lameness, RHpE score, movement of the saddle during ridden exercise, and rider position, balance and size relative to the saddle. Of 148 horses, 28% were lame in hand, whereas 62% were lame ridden. Again, there was a clear link between lameness and the RHpE score.

Ten veterinarians participating in a study to investigate their ability to apply the Ridden Horse Pain Ethogram accurately to twenty horse-rider combinations

In total, data from approximately 1,500 horses have been published in peer reviewed studies, including non-lame horses, lame horses, and lame horses before and after nerve blocks. The data provide strong evidence that the presence of eight or more behaviours of the 24 listed in the RHpE is likely to reflect the presence of musculoskeletal pain. In a variety of studies involving dressage horses and event horses at competitions, higher RHpE scores have been associated with poorer performance compared with horses with low RHpE scores.

At this point, the RHpE has been used to assess horses of a broad range of ages and training levels which have been trained to work in a 'dressage outline', whilst being ridden on the flat in walk, trot and canter, including transitions between and within paces, and 10 m circles in rising trot, plus more advanced movements if the horse is trained to perform them. It has not yet been validated for use whilst a horse is jumping, or on racehorses, western performance horses, or endurance horses. However, clinical experience indicates that with minor adaptations it remains useful. For example, Icelandic horses are also assessed in tölt.

It is important to recognise that the RHpE (performance check list) allows a rider to differentiate a training problem, perhaps due to lack of clear communication by the rider and/or the horse understanding what is required, or because of a horse's lack of musculoskeletal strength and coordination, from a problem which reflects underlying pain. With correct training progressive improvement in performance should be seen unless there is an underlying problem. Failure to understand cues from the rider may result in one or more behaviours of the RHpE being displayed, but the threshold of 8/24 should not be exceeded. The RHpE can be considered a performance check list.

How to use the RHpE with your own horse

Can anyone use the RHpE? The results of application of the RHpE by 23 different assessors have been documented, including both trained and non-trained assessors, and both veterinarians and non-veterinarians. However, as with any skill, training, and practice are required. In Chapter 3, you will find a list of the 24 behaviours and see photographs illustrating each of the behaviours, to the best of our ability.

Factors that can potentially influence the RHpE

It is important to recognise that there is no way of knowing the source of the pain from the RHpE score. The evidence simply shows that a RHpE score of eight or more out of 24 is indicative of musculoskeletal pain. It is likely that this pain warrants further investigation, bearing in mind that this assessment should include evaluation of tack fit (the bridle and saddle), inspection of the mouth, and determination of the rider's size, morphology and weight distribution.

The size of a rider and their weight distribution may have an influence on the RHpE score. In a study in which six horses were ridden by four riders (light, moderate, heavy and very heavy) in a cross-over design, horses had higher RHpE scores at trot when ridden by the two heavier categories of riders compared with the smaller riders, but generally the RHpE threshold score of 8/24 was not reached. In a second study there was an association between higher RHpE scores and a rider sitting on the caudal one-third of the saddle compared with the middle of the saddle. There was an association between higher RHpE scores and tight tree points of the saddle compared with a well-fitting saddle. Saddle fit for both the horse and the rider are relevant. Improved saddle fit may result in reduction in the RHpE score or a change in which behaviours are manifest. However, if there is an underlying lameness, improving the saddle fit may actually result in the lameness becoming more

A large rider who is sitting over the back of the saddle. The horse's head is above the vertical ≥30°, the ears are back and there is an intense stare.

obvious, because the horse is no longer 'guarding' the back. Remember that 'stiffening' the back (reducing the range of motion) is one of the horse's protective adaptations to forelimb or hindlimb lameness. The RHpE score will continue to suggest the presence of musculoskeletal pain.

Rider skill can change a horse's way of going, but a study found no significant difference in RHpE scores when horses were ridden by a more or less skilled rider. However, the more skilled rider could improve the quality of movement. Nosebands with the potential to limit mouth opening (for example, flash, grackle or drop nosebands) did not prevent this behaviour. There was no difference in how often mouth opening (as defined by the RHpE – separation of the teeth for ten seconds or more) was seen in horses with a noseband with the potential to restrict mouth opening, compared with a correctly fitted cavesson noseband, or with no noseband at all. RHpE scores were lower in lame horses after nerve blocks despite the presence of a bit and / or a potentially restrictive noseband, but the reduction in frequency of the occurrence of mouth opening was less than for some other behaviours.

There are some behaviours that might persist even after effective nerve blocks have removed underlying pain. These include toe drag in both hindlimbs (which paradoxically can be induced by hindlimb nerve blocks), and a crooked tail. Some lame horses which carry their 'head 30 degrees or more in front of the vertical for ten or more seconds' may change after nerve blocks have resolved musculoskeletal pain to carrying their 'head ten or more degrees behind the vertical for ten or more seconds'.

A horse ridden by its normal rider in rising trot. The horse's head is above the vertical ≥30°, the ears are back, there is an intense stare and the mouth is open with separation of the teeth. The upper muzzle is extended.

The same horse as above ridden by a more skilled rider in rising trot. The front of the head is behind the vertical ≥10°. The total Ridden Horse Pain Ethogram score when the horse was ridden by each rider in walk, trot and canter was the same, although individual behaviours changed.

Other factors to consider when assessing ridden horses

There are a variety of factors to consider that were not assessed during the development of the RHpE because horses were assessed under variable environmental conditions and the video recordings were not completely reliable for recording sound. For example, does a horse sweat more than would be expected from the intensity of the work, its fitness level, or the environmental temperature and humidity? Does the horse have a higher respiratory rate than expected? Does the breathing sound unusual, or louder than normal for horses? Does the horse hang on one rein, or is it excessively heavy in the hand (leaning on the bit) or light in the hand (not 'taking' a contact)? All of these could be linked to pain. Repeatedly grinding the teeth can indicate discomfort, as can tension, and the horse's willingness to accept the rider's cues (aids). The saddle consistently slipping to one side has been linked to hindlimb lameness in some horses. Horses often snort or blow when nerve blocks have eased the pain. Pain can come not only from the musculoskeletal system, but also from the mouth, the ears, and internal organs (for example in equine gastric ulcer syndrome). Bear in mind, however, that equine gastric ulcer syndrome can develop secondary to musculoskeletal pain and the links between equine gastric ulcer syndrome and poor performance are not well defined.

In conclusion

> "The Ridden Horse Pain Ethogram is a powerful tool for the assessment of ridden horses and for the identification of likely musculoskeletal pain that merits further investigation and treatment, to improve equine welfare and performance."

Dyson, S. The Ridden Horse Pain Ethogram. Equine Vet. Educ. 2022, 34(7): 372-380. https://doi:10.1111/eve.13468

Saddle slip to the right associated with hindlimb lameness.

TALKING POINTS

1. *How could a scientifically validated measure of pain in ridden horses improve horse welfare?*
2. *What happens when a horse showing pain related behaviour is labelled as being 'naughty', rather than the problem being recognised as pain?*
3. *In what direction would you like the researchers involved with the RHpE to head next?*

CASE STUDY: **JACKO**
By Hayley Redding

"We walked up to the mounting block as usual, when he got down and rolled in his tack..."

Jacko is an Irish Sports Horse gelding, whom Hayley bought as an all-rounder. Cheeky and always willing to please, Jacko proved naturally forward and sensitive to the aids, and with good manners on the ground. The pair enjoyed taking part in all disciplines during their first six months together, until Jacko began displaying unusual behaviours.

"One day, I took Jacko into the arena for a flatwork lesson. We walked up to the mounting block as usual – and he got down and rolled in his tack,"

Hayley Redding and Jacko

recalled Hayley. "After this, he seemed to be nervous; random noises or changes in the arena would make him spook. I continued with my weekly lessons, until one day Jacko refused to move up a pace into trot and threatened to rear.

"Following this episode, Jacko continued to be extremely reluctant to go forward during ridden exercise. He was putting his head up and getting tense and anxious when asked to trot. He became grumpy in the stable and reacted abnormally to palpation of his back."

Hayley had Jacko checked by a saddle fitter, dentist and farrier, as well as a chiropractor, who recommended the gelding be seen by a vet for possible kissing spines. Jacko underwent a lameness assessment, but no lameness was observed. Radiography (x-rays) revealed impinging spinous processes between the fourteenth thoracic vertebra and the first lumbar vertebra, associated with moderate osseous modelling and sclerosis. Osseous modelling means change in shape of the bone, while sclerosis refers to increased whiteness of the bone on an x-ray, in this instance reflecting increased bone thickness.

While not a severe case, Jacko's kissing spines were serious enough to warrant either injections or surgical treatment by interspinous ligament desmotomy. Desmotomy means cutting a ligament. There are ligaments, the interspinous ligaments, that connect adjacent spinous processes. Hayley opted for the surgery.

"Jacko's rehabilitation journey has been a long but worthwhile process, during which I reached out to physiotherapist Sue Palmer for her support on Jacko's rehabilitation. Exercises included a lot of baited stretches from side to side, hand walking, long-reining and hill work, and increasing the length of time per session to ensure a slow and steady progression in his work routine.

"We are now nine months post-surgery and Jacko is an even better horse than he was when I first bought him. He is happy in himself, full of character and absolutely loves his work. I continue to include exercises from Jacko's rehabilitation plan, and regular physiotherapy sessions with Sue, to keep building Jacko's physique and confidence in his movement. We have since had a visit from our saddle fitter, who showed me the dramatic improvement in Jacko's posture and outline since his surgery.

"I keep Jacko's work routine varied to keep him interested, with a lot of pole-work, both ridden and in hand, to encourage him to engage his core muscles and to continue to build muscle. We are now training for our first dressage competition."

SNIPPETS OF SCIENCE

"There is evidence that more than 47% of the sports horse population in normal work may be lame, but the lameness is not recognized by owners or trainers. An alternative means of detecting pain may be recognition of behavioral changes in ridden horses..."

Dyson, S., Berger, J., Ellis, A., Mullard, J. Development of an ethogram for a pain scoring system in ridden horses and its application to determine the presence of musculoskeletal pain. J. Vet. Behav.: Clin. Appl. Res. 2018, 23: 47-57.

"It was concluded that despite limitations in the agreement between untrained observers and the trained assessor, the ethogram is a potentially valuable tool for determining the presence of musculoskeletal pain and may be useful for longitudinal monitoring of improvement in lameness."

Dyson, S., Van Dijk, J. Application of a ridden horse ethogram to video recordings of 21 horses before and after diagnostic analgesia: Reduction in behaviour scores. Equine Vet. Educ. 2020, 32(S10): 104-111. https://doi:10.1111/eve.13029.

"...The Ridden Horse Pain Ethogram was applied retrospectively, by a trained analyst, to video recordings which had been acquired in a standardised fashion. There was a significant association between the Ridden Horse Pain Ethogram score and lameness. Lame horses had higher scores than non-lame horses..."

Dyson, S., Berger, J., Ellis, A., Mullard, J. Behavioural observations and comparisons of non-lame horses and lame horses before and after resolution of lameness by diagnostic analgesia. J. Vet. Behav.: Clin. Appl. Res. 2018, 26: 64-70.

DR JO HOCKENHULL

Dr Jo Hockenhull

Dr Jo Hockenhull BSc (Hons) MSc PhD is a Research Fellow in the Animal Welfare and Behaviour Group, Bristol Veterinary School, University of Bristol, United Kingdom. The Animal Welfare and Behaviour Group's research spans the fundamental studies of behaviour, cognition, emotion and development and validation of animal welfare assessment methodologies. In 2019 a study published by Friere and Nicol ranked the organisation 'the most successful of its kind in the last 50 years'.

Dr Hockenhull says: "Riding your horse provides them with exercise and mental stimulation. It is also one way you can spend time together, building your bond by learning more about each other as you explore new places, try new things and experience different situations. Viewing the relationship as a partnership encourages riders to listen to what their horse is telling them. Communication is two-way, and we need to learn to be more vigilant and responsive when it comes to recognising and acting on what our horse is trying to tell us through their behaviour. All too often we don't listen to what we are being told if it stands in the way of something we want to do or achieve or goes against what we think we know. Pain in horses frequently goes unrecognised and untreated. They are masters of subtle behaviours and mask their pain well. So often we simply don't recognise these behavioural indicators of pain for what they are, if we notice them at all. It is only when the horse is making it as clear as they can that something is wrong that we start to take notice. Learning how to spot signs of pain before it reaches this point is part of our duty of care to the horse as covered by the Animal Welfare Act 2006 (Authors' comment: Or equivalent legislation in countries outside the United Kingdom). We owe it to them to listen to what they are trying to tell us and to give them the benefit of the doubt – what is underlying their behaviour may be pain rather than 'naughtiness'. If I could reach out to horse riders with a slogan, it would be 'Stop. Think. What is my horse trying to tell me?'"

SUZANNE ROGERS

Suzanne Rogers has worked as an international consultant for animal welfare and human behaviour change, and is the co-director of Human Behaviour Change for Animals CIC

Website: www.hbcforanimals.com

Suzanne says: "We love this quote from the late Douglas Adams "It is difficult to be sat on all day, every day, by some other creature, without forming an opinion on them. On the other hand, it is perfectly possible to sit all day, every day, on top of another creature and not have the slightest thought about them whatsoever." Although most horse riders do think about their horses, it is likely that those thoughts are through a lens of cultural and societal norms that suggest that horses enjoy being ridden as much as the humans enjoy riding them. Is this likely to be true? The way most domestic horses are kept compromises their natural behaviour – for example, given the opportunity, horses would range many kilometres each day in a home range, walking and eating as part of a herd. Arguably, therefore, hacking out extends the area horses have access to, and could be positive and enriching for the horse, especially if during that hack the horse is given some autonomy (e.g., perhaps being allowed to forage), and as long as every effort has been made to ensure the horse is mentally and physically fit for hacking. Recognising pain in ridden horses is still filtering down from academics and practitioners to the wider equestrian community, and Human Behaviour Change for Animals uses our voice in the equestrian sector to advocate for the horse whenever we can. If we could have a slogan on a billboard, it might say 'If your horse could speak English, what would they say?'"

CHAPTER 3

The How: Learning To Use
The Ridden Horse Pain Ethogram

*"A horse can lend its rider the speed and strength he or she lacks – but the rider
who is wise remembers it is no more than a loan."*

Pam Brown

LET'S START WITH SOME QUESTIONS:

1. *Is your horse being 'naughty' if he spooks and spins?*
2. *What could you do if your horse is napping?*
3. *Are some horses more reactive than others?*
4. *Have you ever known a horse who is apparently sound, but is clearly uncomfortable?*
5. *List 8 behaviours that you think could indicate pain in ridden horses.*

HOW TO USE THE RIDDEN HORSE PAIN ETHOGRAM

"The ethogram is synergistic. The behaviours seen together produce a combined effect greater than the sum of their separate effects. To quote Aristotle, 'the whole is greater than the sum of their parts'. If one was given the components of a motor vehicle, they would have no value unless they were combined to create a car. A behaviour in isolation does not necessarily denote pain, but behaviours creating a score of eight or more suggest a horse in musculoskeletal pain. I often explain to owners that it's like your driving test. A certain total of minor errors reaches a threshold at which point it becomes a major error, and that equals a failure." Jessica Mullard, equine veterinarian involved in the development of the RHpE.

It takes practice

In this chapter, we take you step by step through how to use the Ridden Horse Pain Ethogram (RHpE), a performance check list, with your horse. There are plenty of reasons you might want to do this, and we discuss some of the many potential applications of the RHpE in Chapter 4. Like most things, application of the RHpE is a skill that you will get better at with practice. It would be unrealistic to expect to find it easy the first few times, so don't be put off by having to put in some effort initially. If you use the RHpE regularly, you will soon find that it becomes natural to look out for the 24 behaviours. Not only that, but you will be making a positive contribution to equine welfare by learning to recognise and address pain at an earlier stage.

Have a checklist

First, you need a checklist of the 24 behaviours, and you need to be fully aware of the definitions of each behaviour. Although each photograph is chosen to illustrate a specific behaviour, you will see that most of the photographs show more than one behaviour. This is one reason why good quality video footage is invaluable, so that you can go through the checklist again and again, especially while you are learning to use the RHpE. Video footage filmed and viewed on a telephone may not be of adequate quality or size for accurate application of the RHpE, unless the horse fills the entire screen.

Take it all into account

Bear in mind that you may need to take other factors into account. For example, a deep surface will cause most horses to disturb the surface and therefore appear as though they are dragging their hind toes. If the bit is too wide, it will seem as though it's being pulled through to one side of the mouth or both. In some horses, the sclera (white of the eye) can be seen even at rest in one or both eyes, and in these horses, exposure of the sclera cannot be counted as a pain behaviour in one or both eyes. A pink muzzle may make it more difficult to recognise opening of the mouth and exposure of the tongue.

Using the RHpE with a friend

Ask the rider to warm the horse up in their usual way. To use the RHpE, once the horse is warmed up, watch the horse go around the periphery of an arena, or an equivalent sized area in a field, on both reins in walk, trot and canter. Make sure that you watch the horse from the side, from in front and from behind on each rein. In a rectangular arena, it is best if you can watch from two different corners. If it's appropriate, observe the horse doing 10 m diameter circles on each rein in rising trot, as figures of eight, making sure that each circle is completed. Make sure that the horse performs several transitions between each pace. If the horse is trained to perform more advanced movements, such as collection or lateral work, then watch the horse perform the full repertoire of movements on each rein.

Watch the horse work (after warming up) for a minimum of five minutes and a maximum of approximately ten minutes. Use a stopwatch when you're measuring behaviours that are time dependent, for example the ears being behind the vertical for five or more seconds. Look at whether behaviours are linked to potentially aversive cues from the rider. For example, does the horse only swish his tail when the rider applies a spur cue? We have observed at Grand Prix dressage level that some horses swish their tail in absolute synchrony with spur cues, without showing other abnormal behaviours, meaning that this is probably not a reflection of an underlying problem. Disregard these behaviours unless they are repeated at other times that are not linked to such a potentially aversive cue. We would not regard a rider's leg cue as an aversive cue – a normal horse should not respond negatively to the application of a leg cue. Remember that several of the definitions state 'repeated', for example, repeated incorrect strike off into canter, repeated exposure of the sclera. If these behaviours happen just once, then they do not count towards the RHpE score, as they do not fit the criteria of the ethogram.

As with any skill, applying the RHpE will get easier, and you will get better with training and practice. If you would like to learn more, there is a growing collection of research and educational material available, including an on-line course and a documentary. Details can be found towards the back of this book (Publications related to the Ridden Horse Pain Ethogram).

THE 24 BEHAVIOURS INCLUDED IN THE RIDDEN HORSE PAIN ETHOGRAM

The 24 behaviours are divided into three categories: facial markers, body markers and gait markers.

Facial markers

1. The ears rotated back behind vertical or flat (both or one only) for five or more seconds, or repeatedly laying the ears flat

Ears back behind vertical; the left ear is lower than the right so the head must be tilted, head behind vertical, intense stare, lips separated exposing teeth, tail swishing.

Ears back behind vertical; head above the vertical ≥30°, intense stare, lips separated exposing the teeth, tail swishing.

Ears back behind vertical, intense stare.

2. The eyelids closed or half closed for two to five seconds

Eyelids semi-closed, ears back, head behind vertical ≥10°, mild head tilt.

Eyelids closed, right ear back, head in front of vertical ≥30°.

Eyelids closed, head slightly behind vertical despite loose reins, ears erect and rotated outwards.

3. Sclera (white of the eye) repeatedly exposed

Left: Sclera exposed, intense stare, head tilted with nose to left, mouth open with separation of the teeth, bit pulled through to the left.

Below: Sclera exposed, head tilt with nose to right.

Sclera exposed, intense stare, head above vertical ≥30°, mouth open with separation of the teeth, exposing the tongue which is still within the oral cavity, tail swishing.

4. An intense stare (glazed expression or 'zoned out') for five or more seconds

Intense stare, ears back behind vertical, front of head slightly behind vertical despite a loose rein.

Intense stare, ears back behind vertical, trunk lean.

Intense stare, ears back behind vertical, tail swishing.

5. **The mouth opening and shutting repeatedly with separation of teeth, for ten or more seconds**

Mouth open with separation of the teeth, head behind vertical ≥10° despite loose reins, intense stare, ears erect with pinnae rotated outwards.

Mouth open with separation of the teeth in downward transition from canter to trot.

Mouth open with separation of the teeth, intense stare, ears erect and rotated outwards, front of head <10° behind vertical.

6. The tongue exposed outside the mouth, protruding or hanging out, and / or moving in and out repeatedly

Tongue hanging out to the right, ears erect and rotated outwards.

Tongue hanging out of the front of the mouth, head behind vertical ≥10°, ears erect.

Tongue out to the left, mouth open with separation of the teeth, intense stare, ears erect and rotated outwards.

7. The bit pulled through the mouth on one side (left or right), repeatedly

Bit pulled through to the left, intense stare, ears erect and rotated outwards.

Above: Bit pulled through to the left, ears erect and rotated outwards.

Left: Bit pulled through to the right, right ear back, intense stare. Right hindlimb is crossing underneath the trunk.

Body markers

8. Repeated changes of head position (up / down, but not in rhythm with trot)

Head tossing up and down.

Head tossing up and down.

Up and down head movement.

9. Head tilted, repeated

Left: Head tilt with nose to the left, intense stare, left ear forward, right ear erect and rotated outwards.

Below: Severe head tilt with nose to the right, right ear back.

Head tilt with nose to the left, intense stare.

10. Head in front of vertical (30 degrees or more) for ten or more seconds

Head in front of vertical ≥30°, ears back, right ear lower than left so head must be tilted, intense stare.

Head in front of vertical ≥30°, sclera exposed, left ear behind vertical.

Head in front of vertical ≥30°, ears back, intense stare, tail swishing.

11. Head behind vertical (10 degrees or more) for ten or more seconds

Head behind vertical ≥10°.

Head behind vertical ≥10°, intense stare, sclera exposed, ears back.

Head behind vertical ≥10°, ears back, intense stare, lips separated exposing the teeth which are not separated, tail swishing.

12. Head position changes regularly, tossed or twisted from side to side, corrected constantly

Head constantly moving from side to side.

Head repeatedly moving from side to side.

Head constantly moving from side to side.

13. Tail clamped tightly to the buttocks on the midline or held to one side (a crooked tail)

Tail clamped tightly to the buttocks on the midline, ears back, intense stare, sclera exposed (but this was present at rest, because the iris is small).

Crooked tail to the left, hindlimb toe drag.

Crooked tail to the left; the saddle has slipped slightly to the right.

14. **Tail swishing large movements: repeatedly up and down / side to side / circular; or during transitions**

Tail swishing during flying changes.

Tail swishing, head in front of vertical ≥30°, mouth open with separation of the teeth.

Tail swishing, left hindlimb toe drag.

Gait markers

15. A rushed gait (frequency of trot steps greater than forty in fifteen seconds); irregular rhythm in trot or canter; repeated changes of speed in trot or canter

Repeated changes of speed in canter, ears back, intense stare, tail swishing.

Repeated changes of speed in canter, ears back, intense stare, bit pulled through to the right; abnormal elevation of the forelimbs.

Repeated changes of speed in trot and canter, ears back, intense stare, head tilt, lips separated exposing the teeth, which were not separated, and the tongue, which was still in the oral cavity.

16. Gait too slow (frequency of trot steps less than thirty-five in fifteen seconds); passage-like trot

Trot rhythm too slow (frequency of trot steps less than 35 in 15 seconds), ears back, intense stare.

Passage-like trot with rhythm too slow (frequency of trot steps less than 35 in 15 seconds).

Trot rhythm too slow (frequency of trot steps less than 35 in 15 seconds), head behind vertical ≥10°, lips separated exposing the teeth which are not separated, tail swish. There was no suspension phase.

17. Hindlimbs do not follow tracks of forelimbs but deviated to left or right; on three tracks in trot or canter

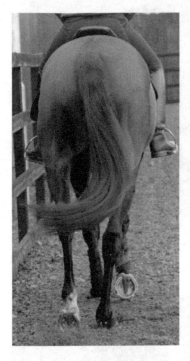

Above: On three tracks in trot, left hindlimb toe drag.

Right: On three tracks in canter with the hindlimbs to the right. Saddle slip to the left.

On three tracks with the
hindlimbs to the left; left
hindlimb toe drag.

18. Canter repeated strike off wrong leg; change of leg in front and / or behind (disunited/ cross-cantering)

Becoming disunited or cross-cantering, intense stare, ears erect and to the side, tail swishing.

Repeated incorrect canter lead, on three tracks, tail swishing, head behind vertical.

Repeatedly changing legs behind in canter, tail swishing, ears back, intense stare, mouth open with separation of the teeth.

19. Spontaneous changes of gait (e.g., breaks from canter to trot, or trot to canter)

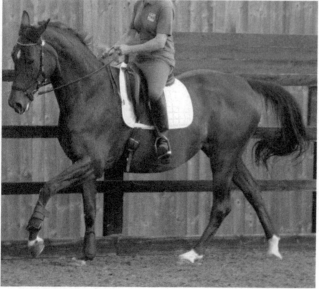

Above: Spontaneously breaking from trot to canter, ears back, intense stare, front of head in front of vertical >30°.

Left: Spontaneous change of gait, breaking from canter to trot, ears back intense stare, tail swishing.

About to break from trot to walk spontaneously, head tilt, mouth open with separation of the teeth, intense stare.

20. Stumbles or trips repeatedly; repeated bilateral hindlimb toe drag

Stumbling on the right hindlimb, intense stare, ears erect and rotated outwards.

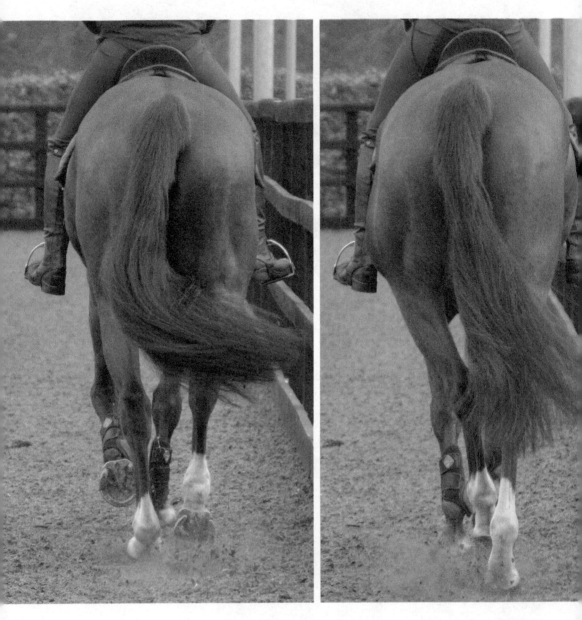

Bilateral hindlimb toe drag, saddle slip to the right.

Left: Left hindlimb toe drag.

Below: Right hindlimb toe drag (the same horse).

21. Sudden change of direction, against rider's direction; spooking

Spooking.

Left: Spooking, tension.

Below: Spooking, tail swishing.

22. Reluctant to move forward (has to be kicked, with or without verbal encouragement), stops spontaneously

Horse reluctant to move forward (has to be kicked, with verbal encouragement), head tilt, intense stare, reluctant to turn to the right.

Horse having to be kicked to try to maintain canter, ears back, intense stare.

Horse stopping spontaneously, resisting, intense stare, lips separated exposing teeth.

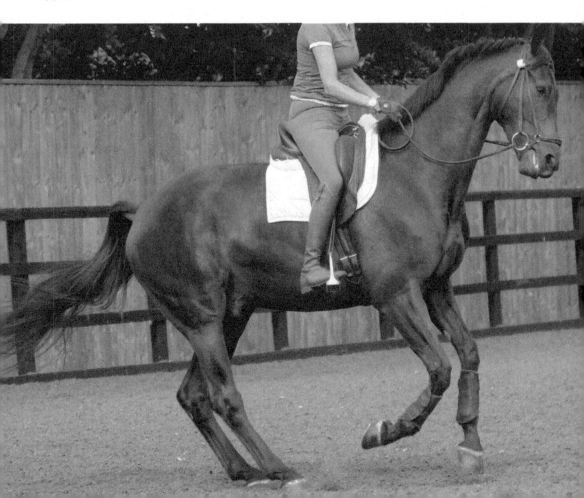

23. Rearing (both forelimbs off the ground)

Rearing, ears back, intense stare.　　Rearing, intense stare.

Rearing, ears
back, intense stare, bit
pulled through to the
right, tail swishing.

24. Bucking or kicking backwards (one or both hindlimbs)

Bucking, exposure of sclera, bit pulled through to right, lips retracted to expose closed teeth.

Above: Bucking, ears back, intense stare.

Left: Bucking and kicking out with the right hindlimb, ears back, intense stare.

Remember that all the behaviours have equal weighting. It is the total number of behaviours displayed which is important. Each behaviour considered individually could have a variety of potential causes. Display of one behaviour only, such as rearing, may not be pain-induced, although it may reflect a training problem, or a previous response to pain that has become habitual. However, a RHpE score of at least 8/24 is highly likely to reflect musculoskeletal pain. A progressive rise in the RHpE score over time is likely to reflect the insidious onset of discomfort. When learning a new movement that a horse finds physically difficult it may initially show some conflict behaviours which were not apparent under other circumstances. Persistence of these behaviours is likely to reflect discomfort. An appropriately trained pain-free horse should be able to learn new movements within two weeks, although may take longer to develop adequate musculoskeletal strength and coordination to perform the movement with better quality and consistency of the gait.

There are also other factors to consider which may reflect musculoskeletal pain which are not included in the RHpE. These include teeth grinding, an increase in blink rate, sweating disproportionately to the exercise intensity, fitness of the horse and the environmental conditions; abnormally high respiratory and heart rates and slow recovery after exercise; abnormal breathing noises; and 'cold-backed' behaviour (dipping the back when first mounted). Other abnormal behaviours include attempting to bite the chest, repeatedly yanking down on the reins, 'hanging on the reins' or a failure to 'take a contact'. At the end of exercise, it is not normal for a horse to stand with the thoracolumbar region (back) extended and the forelimbs and/ or the hindlimbs outstretched.

Abnormal behaviour when tacking-up (for example, fidgeting, picking up a forelimb or hindlimb, turning the head towards the girth region, laying the ears back, repeatedly opening the mouth, rubbing the nose on the wall) and mounting (for example, unwillingness to approach the mounting block or not wanting to stand to be mounted) may also be indicative of anticipation of pain during ridden exercise.

It is important to recognise what normal feels like. A normal horse should feel the same when you sit on the left or right diagonals in rising trot. The horse's rhythm or 'frame' should not change in sitting trot compared with rising trot. There should be similar rein tension in the left and right reins. In canter you should feel that your pelvis is being rocked backwards and forwards and is not being rotated. You should not get a jarring sensation through your back. The horse should turn with similar ease to the left and to the right. You should feel that you are able to apply leg cues without the horse over-reacting.

TALKING POINTS

1. *How does it make you feel, seeing the pictures of horses demonstrating behaviours that are related to pain?*
2. *How does it look to an outsider, when a horse which is objecting to ridden work is forced to comply?*
3. *How could we use the RHpE to improve the image of equestrianism, to show the public how deeply we care for our horses?*

CHAPTER 4

The When and Why:
Uses Of The Ridden Horse Pain Ethogram

"The essential joy of being with horses is that it brings us in contact with the rare elements of grace, beauty, spirit, and freedom."
Sharon Ralls Lemon

LET'S START WITH SOME QUESTIONS:

1. *What emotions do you feel when you see a horse that is clearly in pain during ridden work?*
2. *How would you feel if your instructor suggested that you get someone to check your horse out because he looked like he's in pain?*
3. *Would you expect your farrier or saddle fitter to let you know if they felt there was something wrong with your horse?*
4. *How would you tell a friend that you're concerned their horse might be uncomfortable?*
5. *How could use of the RHpE fit into the routine management of your horse?*

PUTTING THE RIDDEN HORSE PAIN ETHOGRAM TO GOOD USE

Recognising that there is a problem

372

EQUINE VETERINARY EDUCATION
Equine vet. Educ. (2022) **34** (7) 372-380
doi: 10.1111/eve.13468

Review Article

The Ridden Horse Pain Ethogram

S. Dyson (iD)

The Cottage, Market Weston, Diss, UK
Corresponding author email: sue.dyson@aol.com

Keywords: horse; lameness; canter; behaviour; saddle-fit; rider skill

Summary

The Ridden Horse Pain Ethogram (RHpE) comprises 24 behaviours, the majority of which are at least 10 times more likely to be seen in lame horses compared with non-lame horses. The observation of ≥8/24 behaviours is likely to reflect the presence of musculoskeletal pain, although some lame horses score <8/24 behaviours. A marked reduction in RHpE scores after resolution of lameness using diagnostic anaesthesia proves a causal relationship between pain and RHpE scores. Horses should be assessed for approximately 10 min in walk, trot (including 10 m diameter circles), canter and transitions. The validity of the RHpE has been verified for use in horses which perform dressage-type movements, and which have been trained to work with the front of the head in a vertical position. It has not, as yet, been used in horses while jumping, racehorses, western performance or endurance horses. The RHpE provides a valuable tool for riders, trainers, veterinarians and other equine professionals to recognise the presence of musculoskeletal pain, even if overt lameness cannot be recognised. Riders with a higher skill-level may improve gait quality, but cannot obscure behavioural signs of pain, although specific behaviours may change. Tight saddle tree points, the rider sitting on the caudal third of the saddle and rider weight may influence RHpE scores. Accurate application of the RHpE requires training and practice. The RHpE is a powerful tool for the assessment of ridden horses and the identification of likely musculoskeletal pain. Such pain merits further investigation and treatment, to improve equine welfare and performance. The RHpE provides an additional means of evaluating the response to diagnostic anaesthesia. It provides a mechanism for client education and a diplomatic way of communicating with clients about equine discomfort related to saddle-fit, rider size, their position in the saddle and ability to ride in balance.

This commissioned article reviews the development of the Ridden Horse Pain Ethogram (RHpE) and its validation. It describes how and when to use the RHpE and discusses the current evidence about factors other than musculoskeletal pain which may influence RHpE scores.

What is the Ridden Horse Pain Ethogram?

An ethogram is a catalogue of behaviours, each with strict definitions (Grier 1984). The RHpE comprises 24 behaviours, the majority of which are at least 10 times more likely to be seen in a lame horse compared with a non-lame horse (Dyson *et al.* 2018a). The presence of eight or more of these behaviours is likely to reflect the presence of musculoskeletal pain. Different horses react to musculoskeletal pain in a

variety of ways, therefore the spectrum of behaviours demonstrated does not indicate the specific source(s) of pain, although pilot observations using principal component analysis suggest that clusters of behaviours may occur together (Dyson and Ellis 2022).

Why was the RHpE developed?

There is a high frequency of occurrence of lameness in the ridden sports horse population, which is apparently unrecognised by owners (Greve and Dyson 2014; Dyson and Greve 2016). Abnormalities of canter, for example close spatial and temporal placement of the hindlimbs or the lack of a suspension phase (Barstow and Dyson 2015; Boado *et al.* 2020; Greve and Dyson 2020), are frequently overlooked. There appears to be an ethos in the horse world for blaming ridden horse performance problems on the horse's behaviour, the rider's inadequacies, or faults in training, rather than considering that a problem may reflect musculoskeletal pain. From a welfare perspective, there was a clear need to provide a new tool to facilitate owner recognition of the presence of underlying discomfort. This problem is not unique to the horse and there is an increasing recognition in other species, such as the dog and cat, that alterations in behaviour are often a manifestation of pain (Mills *et al.* 2020).

The majority of veterinarians have received little training in the recognition of low-grade lameness, the ways in which ridden horses adapt to musculoskeletal pain (Greve and Dyson 2020), and the influence that discomfort can have on ridden horse performance. Some owners who do recognise that their horse may show signs of an underlying pain-related problem have faced frustration, because many veterinarians have shown a lack of ability to recognise ridden horse performance problems, or have received inadequate training for assessment of ridden horse problems. The potentially unnecessary expense of whole-body skeletal scintigraphy, which frequently provides misleading results (Quiney *et al.* 2018), the conclusion that a problem is solely behavioural, or the advice to 'ride him through it', creates distrust in the profession's ability to provide answers. The use of objective gait analysis in ridden horses remains in its infancy and measurement of gait asymmetry in hand does not necessarily translate to ridden horse performance. Moreover, a horse with either bilateral or multilimb lameness may show no obvious asymmetry (Buchner *et al.* 1995; Bragança *et al.* 2016; Greve *et al.* 2017). In addition, a subjectively non-lame horse, selected based on a comprehensive lameness examination, may exhibit gait asymmetry above the objective threshold defined for lameness (Greve and Dyson 2016). Thus, a tool

As a rider, you have a moral responsibility to recognise that there is a problem, to do your best to identify the cause, and to treat the root cause of the problem. Appropriate treatment, alongside adjusting the management and training if needed, can improve both welfare and performance. Even if a horse is not lame in hand, it may be lame or uncomfortable when it is ridden. The sooner that you recognise and investigate the pain, the more likely it is that you can successfully resolve it. Too many problems are, and have historically been, labelled as being down to the training, down to the rider, down to the horse's behaviour, or simply 'that's just how the horse has always been'. These include common behaviours such as resisting the rider, spookiness, tension, swishing the tail and tilting the head. How many of these are actually pain related?

This is not to imply that there are no difficult horses. Some challenging horses show just one or two behavioural problems, for example rearing or bucking. However, most horses labelled as 'naughty' show many behavioural signs, which is indicative of underlying pain. Each horse reacts as an individual, and pain thresholds vary among horses. The behaviour that a horse shows does not necessarily indicate the source of the discomfort. Some horses are more tolerant of pain than others, and some are more willing than others to do what is asked of them, despite underlying discomfort. Pain and behaviour can be affected by the type and variety of work that a horse is asked to do. You need to see the full repertoire of movements that a horse is asked to perform, to accurately assess its ridden behaviour.

How happy are equine athletes?

In the study 'How Happy Are Equine Athletes', the authors point out that, "To help stakeholders conduct valid and reliable welfare assessments on their horses throughout their lives, the use of available tools by owners, riders, trainers etc. needs to be feasible under everyday conditions." A 'stakeholder' is anyone who has an interest in the horse's quality of life. The stakeholder, in this case, is you. You, as the horse's owner, or rider, or trainer, or veterinarian, or farrier, or physical therapist, or saddle fitter, or dental technician, or nutritionist, or whatever your role is in doing your best for a horse. There was much discussion around the need for more research before welfare can be formally assessed, how a horse's quality of life could be measured, how change over time would be accounted for, and who would do the measuring. The research talked about how consistency could be ensured, and which aspects would be measured.

A valid and reliable tool

That's where use of the Ridden Horse Pain Ethogram (RHpE), a performance check list, comes in. It is a valid and reliable tool that can feasibly be used, in the real world, throughout a horse's life, under everyday conditions. It enables you to use your horse's ridden work as an assessment of how comfortable or uncomfortable it is, from a musculoskeletal perspective. If you can ride your horse in walk, trot and canter, in straight lines and on circles, then you can use the RHpE to help you recognise whether your horse is in any significant level of pain or discomfort. Think of it as a performance check list. If you are confident that the horse is not in any significant pain, then we believe you can reasonably assume that he is comfortable enough, at least from a musculoskeletal standpoint, to do the amount, level, type, and intensity of work that you are asking of him.

When could you use the Ridden Horse Pain Ethogram?

We cannot express strongly enough how important we feel it is to assess a horse regularly during ridden work using the RHpE. Here are just a few suggestions of how, when and why this might be helpful. We're confident that you will come up with ideas of your own, and that use of the RHpE will develop over time as the evidence evolves.

• As a leisure rider

As a leisure rider, you want to be confident that your horse is not in unnecessary pain or discomfort. A better understanding of the signs and symptoms of pain in ridden horses can give you this confidence. Whilst the RHpE cannot give you any guarantees, it is a scientifically validated measure that you, as an owner, can use alongside the information from your horse's team, to help you reach a conclusion.

- As a competition rider

As a competition rider, recognising early symptoms of pain and discomfort means recognising early aspects of performance that could potentially be improved. The RHpE will often flag up musculoskeletal pain that has not yet, or that would not, show up as conventional lameness. Addressing these early signs could give those marginal gains that make the difference between first and second place. Studies of low-level event horses to 5* three-day event horses and Grand Prix dressage horses competing internationally have shown that horses with low RHpE scores perform the best.

- As a work rider

Perhaps, as a rider, you would like to do a regular assessment to check for musculoskeletal pain in the horses you are riding. Once a month, you could arrange for someone to video record ten minutes of your ridden session on each horse. You can include walk, trot, canter, straight lines and circles, transitions and changes of pace within the pace. These videos will not only give you a record of the horse's progress in terms of work quality, but also an opportunity to apply the RHpE and score the horse accordingly. It can be difficult to know what is a training problem that compromises performance, as opposed to an underlying physical problem. The training is, of course, influenced by the skill of the rider, the demeanour of the horse, and the fit of the tack for the horse and the rider. However, if there is a training problem, we would expect to see progressive improvement with practice. If the RHpE score is eight or more, or RHpE scores are progressively increasing over time but are below the threshold of 8/24, then it is likely that there is underlying pain affecting the horse's ability to work. A training problem should not be associated with ongoing behavioural signs linked to pain.

A horse with bilateral forelimb lameness. Compare the rider's position before (top image) and after (bottom image) nerve blocks have abolished the lameness. The rider's upper body position has improved after the nerve blocks compared with before. The horse also shows greater forelimb extension after abolition of lameness.

- As a trainer, coach, or instructor

As a trainer, coach or instructor, you might be concerned that a horse you are working with is not performing as it should be. Using the RHpE gives you an opening to discuss particular behaviours with the owner or rider, and a method of monitoring them over time. Perhaps you could also apply the RHpE with the usual rider, and also with a professional rider, and note whether the RHpE scores are similar for both. We know that a horse with or without musculoskeletal pain, will have a similar RHpE score with different riders, although the specific behaviours shown might change. The more skilled rider may improve the quality of the gaits of a non-lame or lame horse, but sometimes, paradoxically lameness may become apparent or more obvious because a horse is being asked to work harder.

- As a veterinarian

For veterinarians, the RHpE could become a standard part of a lameness work-up when evaluating horses ridden. The horse can be ridden by the usual rider, and / or by a rider employed by the veterinary practice. There is strong evidence that the RHpE is a valid and reliable tool for recognising musculoskeletal pain in ridden horses. There is clear evidence that many horses are apparently sound in hand, even after flexion tests, and also trotting in a small circle on a soft or firm surface, and yet they show pain when they are ridden, manifest as performance problems for the riders. A low-grade forelimb lameness seen only on the lunge

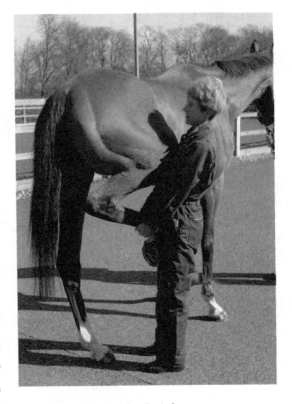

An upper hindlimb flexion test

on a firm or hard surface may not be the cause of the horse's problems that a rider is experiencing during ridden exercise. The horse might be lame on more than one limb, or it might be bilaterally lame (lame on the left and right forelimbs, or the left and right hindlimbs), and that might make lameness difficult to detect. Sometimes, the level of lameness (the lameness grade) is so low that it's hard for a non-specialist equine veterinarian to recognise the lameness, or to think that they can get clear results from a nerve block. However, if the horse is carefully observed during ridden exercise, lameness may become more obvious, and/or it may be easier to recognise restrictions in gait such as limited hindlimb impulsion. Studies have shown that when nerve blocks effectively remove the pain, the RHpE score goes down. Therefore, the RHpE is an extra tool that can help in both identifying the presence of a problem and interpreting the response to nerve blocks.

- As a saddle, bridle or bit fitter

On the previous page, a horse being ridden in its normal saddle which had tight tree points. The horse's ears are back; there is an intense stare and the tail is swishing. Above is the same horse, after change to a better fitting saddle. The horse has a longer stepping forelimb gait and the right hindlimb comes further forward under the trunk. The ears are erect. The eye does not have an intense stare and there is no tail swishing.

As a saddle, bridle or bit fitter, you could use the RHpE during the fitting process. You could ask the rider to walk, trot, and canter, and to include straight lines and circles, a figure of eight using 10 m diameter circles in rising trot, transitions, and changes of pace within the pace. Scoring the horse using the RHpE before and after the changes that you make in the saddle or bridle, or in different saddles, bits, or bridles that the rider is considering, could give you an objective measure to discuss with the owner. This adds weight to your professional judgement, and to the rider's perceived 'feel' of how comfortable their horse is and how well it goes.

- As someone who works in the equine industry

As a physical therapist, farrier, equine dental technician, behaviourist, nutritionist, or other equine professional, you could ask your client to send you a video recording of the horse in ridden work before you visit. You could use the RHpE to determine if there are changes between before and after you have worked with the horse, or to help decide whether the horse needed treatment, or to recommend referral to another member of the horse's team. The RHpE flags up musculoskeletal pain in ridden horses, and your work may have an impact on that.

- When you're buying a new horse

At a pre-purchase examination (vetting), both the potential purchaser and the veterinarian could score the horse according to the RHpE. This would add to the information used to decide whether or not to buy the horse. Take that a step further, and you could apply the RHpE to a video recording of a horse you were considering viewing prior to purchase, rather than driving hundreds of miles only to be disappointed as soon as you see the horse ridden. A professional rider selling a horse might be able to improve the quality of a horse's movement, but they will not be able to affect the RHpE score and conceal signs indicative of musculoskeletal pain.

It can be the case that a horse is coping at its current work level, with the regular rider, and appears to be sound, but it shows behavioural signs of discomfort. When buying a new horse, a RHpE score of eight or more should be regarded as a warning sign that a high level of maintenance is likely to be required. It is also possible that with a change in ownership and therefore management (for example, turnout, level and type of work, consistency of work, farriery, saddle fit, rider skill level, type of work surface, dentistry, feed, and more), the problem(s) could get worse.

- To reduce the risk of injury

A horse which is in pain is at greater risk of injury, either to itself or to the rider. This could be through a gradual process of degenerative changes leading to significant pathology (damage to a joint, tendon, or ligament, for example). Early recognition of discomfort can help with early diagnosis, which means a greater likelihood of successful treatment. The higher risk of injury might be due to the increased likelihood of spooky, sharp behaviour in horses which are in musculoskeletal discomfort. Sore horses are at a greater risk of tripping, either in front or behind, which could result in injury to both the horse and the rider. A horse which has adapted its movement in the face of pain in order to minimise discomfort often becomes more uncomfortable for the rider; for example, reduced range of motion of the horse's back results in an increase in jarring motion through the rider's back, most particularly in canter.

- To improve performance

A horse jumping well and in harmony with a happy rider

Studies show that the social licence to compete in upper-level dressage and in eventing is supported by low RHpE scores. However, there is a higher frequency of lameness in lower-level event horses. At both high and low levels of competition high RHpE scores were generally associated with lower finish places or failure to complete. Identifying, investigating and treating horses with high RHpE scores, lameness, or abnormalities of canter could improve performance as well as welfare.

- To improve welfare

Horses enjoying a pleasure ride

Moving aside from the clear benefits in owner confidence, safety, quality of performance, behaviour, and welfare, we have a moral and ethical duty to care for our horses. All too often, horses which 'misbehave' in their ridden work are punished for doing so. We have both seen many, many cases where that 'misbehaviour' is very likely due to musculoskeletal pain. The horse can only communicate his pain or discomfort through his behaviour or performance. It is your job to listen, and the RHpE gives you a tool to do this.

- To maintain equestrianism's social license to operate

One of the focus group participants in the study 'How Happy Are Equine Athletes?' stated, "The things mentioned in other disciplines—whips, spurs, tight nosebands—these were all things seen in the public eye that come to the attention of the public as signs of negative welfare and while rightly so, it almost takes the spotlight off the other 23 hours of the horses' lives and how they are being managed the rest of the time when they are not in the public eye." Competitions are a showcase, and what goes on at home is equally, if not more, important. Ridden work and training make up only a small portion of a horse's life, but for most domestic horses, it's a significant part. It is not OK for horses to suffer punitive training techniques, such as being repeatedly hit with a whip, or 'tied down' with gadgets.

As discussed earlier, equestrianism's social licence is at risk. It is your responsibility to educate yourself, and to keep up to date with the latest knowledge so that you can use this in your decision-making around the management and training of your horse.

- To assess external factors

There are other factors that might influence whether a horse demonstrates specific behaviours defined in the RHpE. These include the skill level of the rider, the rider's size and position in the saddle, the fit of the tack, and other sources of pain, for example gastric ulceration. If a ridden horse is experiencing musculoskeletal pain the rider's skill level may affect the behaviours that the horse shows, although the total RHpE score will remain similar and still reflect musculoskeletal pain. For example, with a less skilful rider the horse may have the front of the head in front of a vertical position ($\geq 30^0$ for ≥ 10s) whereas

with a more skilled rider the front of the head may be behind a vertical position ($\geq 10^0$ for $\geq 10s$).

It should be noted that there is limited evidence that gastric ulceration is a primary cause of poor performance; there is an increasing body of evidence that chronic musculoskeletal pain may predispose to the development of gastric ulceration. Management of musculoskeletal pain is crucial for the successful long-term management of gastric ulceration.

A horse with poor performance that had been attributed to gastric ulcers, but no improvement had been seen in the performance after treatment of the ulcers. The right ear is back, the head is tilted with the nose to the right and the right hindlimb is crossing under the trunk.

A tool to recognise underlying pain

The RHpE is a tool you can use to help you recognise that a horse may have underlying pain. Some horses seem able and willing to perform adequately even with discomfort, others not so. This depends on many factors, including: the athletic ability of the horse, the level at which it is being asked to perform, the variety of the work pattern, the surfaces on which the horse is working, the skill, balance and size of the rider, the temperament of the horse and the level of discomfort. Other management factors, such as daily turnout and social interactions with other horses, are also potentially important. If a horse shows eight or more of the 24 behaviours listed in the RHpE, then further investigation is warranted.

Above: Ears back, an intense stare, the front of the head is >30° in front of the vertical and the tail is swishing. The Ridden Horse Pain Ethogram score was 9/24, indicating the likely presence of musculoskeletal pain.

Left: A horse warming up for the dressage phase of Badminton three-day event. This is a picture of harmony and athleticism.

To maintain social licence to operate in the world of equestrian sport, we must demonstrate that horses are free from unnecessary pain. Reducing levels of pain leads to improved performance and better results, as well as making the sport safer for both horses and riders. Less pain leads to an improved demeanour, which is suggestive of a 'happier' horse. A more comfortable horse becomes more comfortable to ride. This enables the rider to be in a better position (see images on page 100) and get improved responses to cues. The horse becomes more rideable. As equestrians, we have moral and ethical responsibilities to do our best for horses. There is always more to know, and as we understand and learn more about our horses' behaviour, we can improve welfare, safety and performance.

CASE STUDY: **COPPER**
By Rachel

The names of both horse and owner have been changed to provide anonymity

"I was desperate to get to the bottom of why my seemingly sound mare who loved her job had become literally unrideable.

Trust your gut! If you think your horse feels wrong, you are probably right!"

Rachel and Copper

Rachel bought Copper as a five-year-old, having loved her athleticism and technique over fences. Copper's conformation was not perfect, but she was sound and competing well, and Rachel purchased her following a successful five-stage vetting. Rachel competed Copper in affiliated showjumping and eventing for two seasons, culminating in winning an Area Eventing championship, before turning her away for a winter holiday. When work resumed the following season, Copper began to show resistance when ridden.

"She was lacking impulsion and suspension in canter and had a tendency to hollow in transitions to canter," said Rachel. "I could feel a slight difference when I changed diagonals in trot. In canter she would sometimes become disunited, and occasionally she would pull herself up in canter, and was reluctant to move forwards.

"I also noticed a change in her posture whilst at rest. She was always resting a hind leg and pointing the diagonal foreleg, often shifting her weight from one hind leg to the other like she couldn't get comfy."

Copper's regular physiotherapist found her reactive under the front of the saddle and also found increased muscle tension behind the saddle. It was discovered that the ends of the adjustable gullet of the saddle were digging in. Over several months, Rachel used three saddle fitters in an effort to find a saddle comfortable for Copper. The mare appeared to be extremely sensitive to saddle fit and flocking, and even after buying a made to measure saddle, the behavioural problems when ridden persisted.

Copper was sent for veterinary assessments, including gastroscopy, but no ulcers were seen. No lameness was detected. At a subsequent reassessment mild hindlimb lameness was observed and attributed to suspensory ligament strain. There was also pain on palpation over Copper's sacroiliac region. Both hindlimb suspensory ligaments were medicated, and a week later the vet declared Copper to be pain-free and recommended that Rachel should work with an ACPAT (Association of Chartered Physiotherapists in Animal Therapy) physiotherapist on a back-to-work plan.

"The physiotherapist used muscle electrostimulation on Copper's back behind the saddle and concluded that as the mare didn't overly mind this being done, it was evidence of no significant issue. She advised me to rehabilitate the horse using a programme of raised pole exercises on the lunge. Being athletic and careful, Copper performed the exercises easily."

However, when ridden work resumed, Copper displayed the same behavioural problems. The vet deemed a rescan and ridden assessment unnecessary. Nerve blocks of the hindlimb suspensory ligaments did not result in a difference in Copper's movement in hand. An equine orthopaedic specialist vet also found no lameness and suggested to Rachel that Copper's poor performance could be a training issue.

Copper was referred for a bone scan, which showed 'hot spots' in the articular processes of the vertebrae under the saddle. Hot spots refer to areas of increased radiopharmaceutical uptake, indicating abnormal bone activity, but they do not necessarily equate with the sites being a source of pain. The articular process joints were x-rayed, but no abnormalities were detected. Nonetheless, Copper's spine was medicated, and she was sent home to recommence rehabilitation work.

"Sadly, Copper's ridden behaviour continued to deteriorate. She was so distressed at the prospect of being ridden, she started to dig up her bed when I put her tack on the door. Yet, she always went beautifully on the lunge and long reins and had no problems loose jumping – the behavioural issues were only apparent with the weight of a rider."

Rachel found an article by Sue Dyson regarding sacroiliac injury and recognised some of the signs described within the article in Copper. Her vet found no evidence of pain in the mare's sacroiliac region but agreed to medicate the area. Although initially Copper appeared happy, by day three of ridden work she was stalling in walk and threatening to rear. However, the failure to respond to medication does not imply that the treated area is not a source of pain. It may reflect lack of efficacy of the medication.

Copper

"I was desperate to get to the bottom of why my seemingly sound mare who loved her job had become literally unrideable." Rachel decided it was time to drive the long distance to see Sue Dyson in person for an assessment.

After an assessment of the horse's history and a thorough clinical examination, including ridden exercise, Sue concluded that Copper had "several problems contributing to pain, poor performance, bilateral hindlimb lameness and poor hindlimb impulsion including chronic suspensory desmopathy, a substantial component of lumbosacroiliac joint region pain, and epaxial muscle hypertonicity (see full report, page 115).

With a guarded prognosis for returning to full, pain-free athletic activity, Copper was retired from ridden work.

"Trust your gut"

As a professional rider, Rachel has been able to apply her experience with Copper to other horses she works with, and reveals her key learnings:

"Throughout Copper's deterioration, she never refused a jump or hit a pole. Her technique remained exceptional, and vets and physiotherapists used this as evidence there wasn't anything seriously wrong with her. In hindsight, the quality of the canter, which was lacking a suspension phase, and displays of pain were a more appropriate measure of the situation than her jumping performance.

"The presence or absence of 'lameness' is widely used as a measure of pain and 'soundness' in a horse, which does not accurately account for many other types and areas of pain. This needs to change for the welfare of horses everywhere, who are compromised and being expected to perform because vets are unable to diagnose the problem, rather than because there is no problem.

"A ridden assessment, in the horse's usual tack and with the usual rider, should be part of any lameness assessment and be the first port of call, not the last resort.

"Reduced tolerance of saddle fit is an indicator of something else. A pain-free horse will be much better able to tolerate a less than ideal saddle fit. A painful horse is likely to have an altered posture, which will also influence saddle fit.

"A 'training problem' is quite often an indicator of a lameness issue. A good rider can compensate for this more easily than a novice rider, but a sound horse is easier to ride and is probably less likely to experience 'training problems'.

"I have found that horses develop coping mechanisms for pain, such as 'holding themselves'. Physical treatments like massage, and schooling such as stretching, can actually make a horse look less sound because the horse is no longer compensating and is therefore less able to perform.

"How a horse responds to differing ground conditions is a useful indicator. For example, hard ground may aggravate some underlying issues and elicit a pain response that is not seen on soft ground.

"Perceived 'bitting issues' can reflect lameness. As with saddle fit, a sound horse is much more tolerant of bits and a sore horse might 'run through the bridle' or avoid the contact. What the rider feels in the reins is often a consequence of the state of the horse's back.

"In my experience, vets and physiotherapists do not always respect what the rider or handler is experiencing. They can underestimate the value of noticing a change in the horse's behaviour, or even posture at rest, as an indicator of something wrong, Sue Dyson being an exception.

"I have found that a horse being 'lazy' is frequently a primary indicator of pain. In my experience, horses that initially present as 'hard to get in front of the leg' are eventually diagnosed with chronic lameness. Riders and trainers should be more aware of this and see it as a red flag rather than a disobedient horse.

"The first sign of hindlimb lameness the physiotherapist / massage lady found in each case was increased muscle tension behind the saddle, with more tension on the side of the lamer hindlimb.

"Of horses I have ridden that ended up being diagnosed with hindlimb lameness (hind suspensory ligament injuries), I have noticed they 'fishtailed' trotting in straight lines out hacking and wanted to carry their quarters to either side rather than trot straight.

"The lame horses I have ridden have all given me pain after riding them, for example in my sacroiliac joints or lower back. I stop riding the horse and my pain disappears. Horses that are bad in the contact or heavy on the forehand give me shoulder or neck pain. Riders should pay attention to how their bodies feel after riding different horses.

"Regular equine massage or physiotherapy treatments are an excellent way of keeping track of your horse's soundness as they highlight subtle changes in muscle tension and posture, often before there is a behavioural problem or lameness.

"Watching a horse's posture at rest can give a valuable insight into how they are feeling. Any new behaviours, such as pointing a toe or constantly shifting weight, might be the first indicator of a problem brewing.

"A horse that is enjoying what it is doing will perform through the pain, especially with the help of adrenaline and a decent rider. It doesn't mean there isn't pain or underlying injury.

"Sue highlighted that I'm on the tall side for my mare and I should consider riding with longer stirrups so that I'm not sitting so far back, which was really useful to know. (Authors' comment: A change in the position of the stirrup bars can also be helpful, and the appropriate size of saddle flap to accommodate the length of the rider's legs.)

"Trust your gut. If you think your horse feels wrong, you are probably right."

Copper's report from Dr Sue Dyson

"The above horse was examined at Rossdales Diagnostic Centre on 12th March 2021. The case history was assessed and a clinical examination, including ridden exercise, carried out. The horse was slightly overweight (body condition score 7/9). The tubera sacrale were higher than the withers. (Authors' comment: The tubera sacrale are known colloquially as the jumpers' bump.) There was an abnormal reaction to pressure applied over the tubera sacrale. (Authors' comment: Such a reaction often reflects lumbosacroiliac joint region pain.) There was increased epaxial muscle tension in the lumbar region, right > left. (Authors' comment: The epaxial muscles are the 'top line' muscles.) Flexibility of the lumbosacral region was limited.

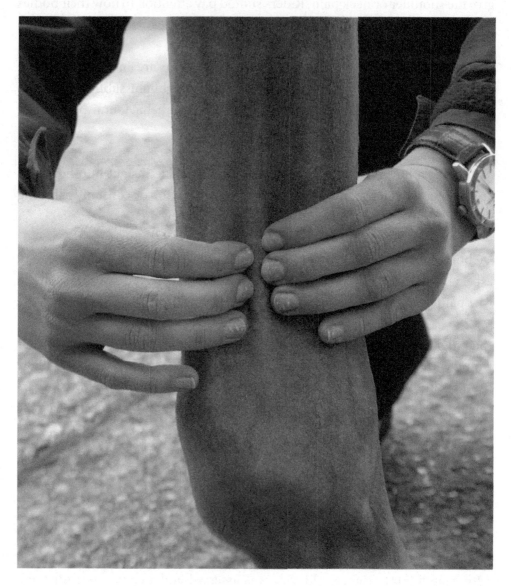

Palpation to assess the size of a suspensory ligament: this is normal

When examined moving in hand on a hard surface at the trot, there was a moderate right hindlimb lameness (grade 3/8). Proximal limb flexion of the left hindlimb reduced the right hindlimb lameness. Other flexion tests did not alter the gait. When lunged on a soft surface, there was reduced range of motion of the thoracolumbosacral region, with exaggerated contractions of the epaxial muscles. There was an inward lean of the trunk and the horse tended to look out. Canter was croup high and on the forehand and crooked. The horse became disunited (cross-cantered) or broke several times.

When ridden, the horse showed left hindlimb lameness (2/8) on the left rein and right hindlimb lameness on the right rein (3/8). She lacked hindlimb impulsion and engagement in both trot and canter. There was reduced range of motion of the thoracolumbosacral region. The saddle slipped to the left on the right rein. The horse showed many behavioural signs consistent with pain, including an intense stare, exposure of the sclera, ears back, requiring verbal encouragement, tail swishing, having an unsteady head carriage, going above the bit, stopping spontaneously and yanking down on the reins, rearing. The horse was reluctant to establish canter, but did so eventually and was then croup high, crooked and above the bit. The rider was well in balance despite sitting on the caudal third of the saddle, associated with her long thigh length.

Right hind plantar (proximal to the digital flexor tendon sheath) and plantar metatarsal nerve blocks did not alter the gait. Perineural anaesthesia of the deep branch of the lateral plantar nerve of the right hindlimb abolished the right hindlimb lameness. Perineural anaesthesia of the deep branch of the lateral plantar nerve of the left hindlimb abolished the left hindlimb lameness. The saddle no longer slipped to the left. The horse was less resistant and maintained a more consistent rhythm in small circles. There was a general improvement in demeanour and a more consistent head and neck carriage in trot. Infiltration of local anaesthetic solution around the sacroiliac joints resulted in substantial further improvement in the quality of both trot and canter and in the horse's behaviour. There was increased range of motion of the thoracolumbosacral region, increased swing of the tail and the horse was straighter in all paces and more forward going and stretched forward and down with the head and neck. The overall improvement compared with baseline was enormous, with the horse's gait quality and behaviour clearly reflecting the reduction in discomfort. It was estimated that there was approximately 40% improvement after the subtarsal nerve blocks and 60% improvement after infiltration of local anaesthetic solution around the sacroiliac joints.

Radiographic examination of the hocks and proximal metatarsal regions was performed. In the left hindlimb, there was smoothly demarcated increased opacity in the proximolateral aspect of the third metatarsal bone, which probably reflects a congenital exostosis. (Authors' comment: A congenital exostosis is a bony lump which has been present since birth and is of unlikely clinical significance.) In the right hindlimb, there was mild increased opacity of the trabecular bone of the central and third tarsal bones. There was very mild modelling of the distal dorsal aspect of the third tarsal bone and the proximodorsal aspect of the third metatarsal bone. These abnormalities are of unlikely current clinical significance.

An ultrasonographic examination of the plantar soft tissue structures of the tarsal and metatarsal regions of both hindlimbs revealed evidence of chronic proximal suspensory desmopathy (right > left), with enlargement of the proximal third of each ligament (right > left), diffuse reduction in echogenicity and loss of long linear parallel echoes in longitudinal images. (Authors' comments: Desmopathy means injury without active inflammation. Echogenicity refers to the white dot pattern of a normal ligament. Reduced echogenicity refers to loss of the regularity of the dot pattern and a grey or black appearance.) In the right hindlimb, there was loss of separation between the suspensory ligament and the accessory ligament of the deep digital flexor tendon, suggestive of adhesion formation. (Authors' comment: The accessory ligament of the deep digital flexor tendon is the check ligament.) Examination per rectum revealed abnormalities of the lumbosacral joint with increased echogenicity of the central portion of the intervertebral disc, surrounded by reduced echogenicity. There was ventral bulging of the disc, with displacement of the ventral longitudinal ligament. There was also loss of echogenicity of the peripheral regions of the intervertebral disc of the articulation between the fifth and sixth lumbar vertebrae.

In conclusion, this horse has several problems contributing to pain and poor performance, bilateral hindlimb lameness and poor hindlimb impulsion associated with chronic suspensory desmopathy (right > left), a substantial component of lumbosacroiliac joint region pain, and right > left epaxial muscle hypertonicity. (Authors' comment: Epaxial muscle hypertonicity means increased tension in the 'top line' muscles.) The latter is probably secondary.

Hindlimb proximal suspensory desmopathy is a challenging condition to manage, with a large proportion of horses treated conservatively having persistent or recurrent lameness. Local injections with corticosteroids or shockwave therapy provide short-term palliative pain-relief only. Treatment with biological preparations (e.g., platelet rich plasma or mesenchymal stem cells) is generally unsuccessful. Laser treatment has not been rewarding. Surgical treatment, by neurectomy of the deep branch of the lateral plantar nerve and plantar fasciotomy of both hindlimbs, gives potentially the best chance of resolution of the hindlimb lameness. However, it must be recognised that although with primary proximal suspensory desmopathy alone, the success of surgery is approximately 78% for return to full athletic function, with coexistent chronic sacroiliac joint region pain the prognosis is substantially reduced (maximum 40%), especially in those horses in which the component of lumbosacroiliac joint region pain exceeds pain associated with hindlimb proximal suspensory desmopathy. The presence of adhesions between the suspensory ligament and adjacent structure may be one of the reasons for surgical failures. The sacroiliac and lumbosacral joints can be treated by medication of using corticosteroids and Sarapin, however the results are variable and unpredictable, especially in a horse with chronic problems. The epaxial muscle hypertonicity may be a reflection of hindlimb lameness or lumbosacroiliac joint region pain.

Overall, the prognosis for a return to pain-free full athletic function must be considered guarded. It seems most likely that this has been an insidiously progressive problem. It was reported that the horse had always tended to be inactive behind in flat work, although had jumped very well. The ability to jump well, particularly when the horse is jumping well within its athletic capacity, does not preclude pain-related limitations in flat work. It is not possible to say which problem arose first. The horse's conformation, the tubera sacrale being higher than the withers, may have been a factor."

LET'S OPEN THIS UP TO A WIDER PERSPECTIVE: TALKING POINTS:

1. *Why is it important that we can recognise when a ridden horse is in pain?*
2. *Are top level competition horses more comfortable in their ridden work than amateur level, or vice versa?*
3. *What could the governing bodies, organisations, associations and charities do to help raise awareness of our ability to recognise pain in ridden horses?*

CASE STUDY: **DIGGER**
By Claire Martin

"I had multiple comments like 'he's so cheeky' and 'you need to push him through the bad behaviour' but I wasn't convinced this was the case."

Digger

Digger was a Warmblood gelding who spent the first two years of his life living out with other young horses, before Claire bought him, aiming for him to be a general all-rounder, with a focus on eventing. He was unbacked but had been well handled and, following a two-stage vetting which focuses on the basics – his heart, lungs and eyes – he came home with Claire.

Claire began teaching Digger basic skills through in-hand work. The gelding was initially challenging, and could be bolshy to handle, but as he built up trust in Claire, his behaviour improved. He was backed and turned away for a few months, before making a successful start to ridden work. He enjoyed plenty of hacking, some dressage competitions and jumping clinics.

But the following year, everything changed as Digger's ridden behaviour began to deteriorate. "He seemed unhappy. When he saw his tack, he would turn away or stand at the back of the stable," said Claire. Avoidance of being tacked-up or abnormal behaviour while being tacked-up or mounted have been shown to be related to an ill-fitting saddle, notably tight tree points, or to musculoskeletal pain. "Under saddle, he started napping and, if pressured, would sometimes buck or rear. I also noticed he started jumping awkwardly. I received multiple comments like, 'He's so cheeky' and, 'You need to push him through the bad behaviour', but I wasn't convinced this was the case."

Claire had a saddle fitter, dentist and physiotherapist check Digger, and although he wasn't overtly lame, she decided to have him investigated for poor performance. Digger underwent a full investigation with Sue Dyson, which included nerve blocking and x-rays, and he was diagnosed with Idiopathic Hopping-type Lameness Syndrome in the Ridden Horse. Idiopathic hopping-type lameness syndrome is an uncommon cause of forelimb lameness, occasionally seen on the lunge, but usually only when ridden. As the affected forelimb moves forwards the head and neck go up, and it may feel as if the horse is trying to break to canter. The lameness may be episodic, with an affected horse moving freely and normally and then suddenly showing hopping steps of variable severity, with a reluctance to go forwards, reflecting the severity of pain. This syndrome can be associated with caudal cervical or cranial thoracic nerve root pain. Lameness may get worse with nerve blocks. Occasionally a saddle with tight tree points can provoke similar but less severe symptoms.

"Unfortunately, the prognosis for this condition is poor, and I was advised it was unlikely Digger would ever be comfortable enough for a ridden career. I decided to try a "bute" [phenylbutazone] trial and six months of field rest, but there was no improvement. As Digger was an excitable, highly-strung horse who thrived off routine and exercise, it was decided the kindest option was to euthanise Digger.

"The RHpE wasn't published when Digger was showing poor behaviour under saddle. However, it would have been a very useful tool in Digger's diagnosis. Although he wasn't obviously lame, Digger showed many of the behaviours explained in the ethogram.

"As a coach, rider, and veterinary physiotherapist, I now regularly use the RHpE and find it so useful. I certainly hope to see it becoming a widely used tool to help further improve equine welfare."

SNIPPETS OF SCIENCE

"The objectives of this study were to compare horses' gaits in hand and when ridden; to assess static and dynamic saddle fit for each horse and rider; to apply the Ridden Horse Pain Ethogram (RHpE) and relate the findings to gait abnormalities consistent with musculoskeletal pain, rider position and balance and saddle fit; and to document noseband use and its relationship with mouth opening during ridden exercise..."

Dyson, S., Bondi, A., Routh, J., Pollard, D. Gait abnormalities and ridden horse behaviour in a convenience sample of the United Kingdom ridden sports horse and leisure horse population. Equine Vet. Educ. 2022, 34: 84-95. https://doi: 10.1111/eve.13395

"...The aim of this study was to further test the Ridden Horse Pain Ethogram by applying it to a convenience sample (n = 60) of sports horses and riding school horses in regular work and assumed by their owners to be working comfortably..."

Dyson S, Pollard D. Application of a Ridden Horse Pain Ethogram and its relationship with gait in a convenience sample of 60 riding horses. Animals 2020,10(6):1044. https://doi:10.3390/ani10061044.

"...The RHpE should facilitate earlier identification of horses which may benefit from diagnosis and treatment, resulting in improvement in both performance and equine welfare."

Dyson, S., Ellis, A. Application of a Ridden Horse Pain Ethogram to horses competing at 5-star three-day-events: comparison with performance. Equine Vet. Educ. 2022, 34(6): 306-315. https://doi: 10.1111/eve.13415

DR TAMZIN FURTADO

Dr Tamzin Furtado

Dr Tamzin Furtado is a social scientist with a background in global health and has a specific interest in the interconnections between human and animal health and wellbeing. She completed a PhD at the University of Liverpool studying how we can improve the management of obesity in horses, particularly focusing on horse-human relationships and human behaviour change.

How do we know if our competition horses are "happy equine athletes"?

- A short summary of a research study, by Dr Tamzin Furtado, University of Liverpool

Dr Furtado says: "The "Happy Athlete" research study was conducted because there is a real lack of information about how different stakeholders in equestrian sport view equine well-being within the competition environment. While racing has been quite extensively studied, other equestrian sports have been overlooked, despite a very clear changing public perception about the use of animals in sports. As a result, the study team wanted to bring together riders, judges, trainers, grooms, and others from across different equestrian disciplines to hear their views on equine welfare within those sports. A workshop was held in March 2021, bringing together participants from endurance, eventing, showjumping, dressage, carriage driving, polo and racing, alongside academics and welfare staff.

The research highlighted that all stakeholders wanted the best for their horses and believed that horses could enjoy and have good welfare within a competitive lifestyle; in particular, sports horses' physical health was often carefully attended to. However, participants felt that the demands of competition could sometimes be detrimental to welfare; for example, when horses were pushed to higher level competitions too quickly, or disallowed time to "be a horse", for example by spending time turned out in a field with friends. Importantly, participants described differing potential welfare issues across all the sports studied, despite the fact that some (e.g., dressage) have a trained observer looking for signs of discomfort, and others (e.g., endurance) include multiple veterinary checks. Additionally, participants discussed that improved competition rules designed to improve welfare, such as rules about noseband tightness, did not address more major contributors to welfare, such as the horse's management and training at home.

The respondents highlighted some findings that may be of use to other competitive participants: because of the multiple conflicting demands placed on sports horse stakeholders, it was seen as important to work as a team to evaluate the well-being of individual horses. Listening to the opinions of grooms, veterinarians, riders, trainers, physiotherapists, and others could help to bring together an unbiased view on how horses are coping with the demands of competition. Secondly, few participants had made use of formal welfare monitoring tools or training logs for their horses, but they agreed that such tools could potentially help to monitor how horses changed over time, thereby helping to catch any issues at an early stage.

The take-home message from this research is that, when competing, it is natural for us to get side-tracked by our human wants and needs – and that applies whatever your role is in equestrian sport. However, through working collaboratively as a team with the professionals around that horse (including veterinarians, farriers, instructors, trainers, grooms etc.), and carefully monitoring changes over time, we stand a better chance of noticing when horses are struggling to cope, emotionally and physically. Moreover, allowing horses management which gives them time to "be horses" – spending time with friends in a spacious environment such as a field, pays dividends to their well-being overall."

Furtado, T., Preshaw, L., Hockenhull, J., Wathan, J., Douglas, J., Horseman, S., Smith, R., Pollard, D., Pinchbeck, G., Rogers, J., Hall, C. How happy are equine athletes? Stakeholder perceptions of equine welfare issues associated with equestrian sport. Animals 2021, 11: 3228. https://doi.org/10.3390/ani11113228

CHAPTER 5

Ask The Experts

"There is something about the outside of a horse that is good for the inside of a man."
Sir Winston Churchill

CASE STUDY: **JONNY**
By Thea Roberts

"Jonny felt like he was running out of steam. People said it was just because it was hot, but I felt there were too many things adding up."

Thea Roberts and Jonny

"I bought 10-year-old Irish Sports Horse Jonny because he was a kind horse with a good brain, who I hoped would take me to BE90 level in eventing," said Thea. "A late starting eventer, I started eventing aged forty-four years. I'd describe myself as a leisure rider who likes to compete. After spending years riding at riding schools, I bought my first horse eleven years ago. After my horse of a lifetime, Valco, passed away, I bought Jonny for hacking, Riding Club activities and low-level British Eventing. He was described as 'sometimes a bit lazy' but was a delightful horse and very chilled. He 'passed' a five-stage vetting, including x-rays of both hocks and both front feet."

Six weeks after Jonny arrived, Thea noticed his head tilting during ridden work, when he was working on the left rein. Over the next three months, a couple of instructors gave some suggestions for ridden techniques to resolve the behaviour. "I was told that he's a big horse, he's easily strung out, that's where he prefers to be, to collect him more, etcetera. There were no alarm bells ringing." Jonny would occasionally stumble in the arena. This always seemed to be in the same spot so was attributed to the footing. Thea also noticed that Jonny seemed to shuffle when walking downhill. Reluctance to walk downhill is usually pain-induced, and often related to front foot pain.

As Jonny gained fitness, he proved to be an athletic jumper with a fantastic brain. However, a few months later he started to become hesitant about going on the lorry. "I thought it was related to having just got a field companion whom he didn't want to leave, and so I thought nothing of it, even though until that point he'd practically loaded himself. Jonny seemed to be fit and healthy and had regular physiotherapy to help maintain his health. I remember, though, the farrier mentioning he struggled a bit when he picked up the right hindlimb.

"The epiphany came at our third BE80 competition, having been well-placed in the first two. At the third, Jonny felt great in the dressage and showjumping, but later, during the warm-up for the cross-country, he didn't feel right; there was no excitement. We went clear but were nearly a minute over the time and Jonny felt like he was running out of steam. People said it was just because it was hot, but I felt there were too many things adding up."

Having heard of the RHpE and been in contact with Sue Dyson, Thea sent her some video footage of Jonny. Features of lameness or behaviours of the RHpE may be missed on video recordings obtained on a smartphone without a zoom facility. The video recordings must be of good quality and viewing video footage full screen on a laptop, tablet or personal computer is strongly recommended.

Sue saw that the gelding was bilaterally lame behind – which was why no lameness had been spotted, because he was lame in both hindlimbs, so he wasn't limping – and he was toe dragging with both hindlimbs. Jonny was referred to Sue for a lameness work up.

"Sue also found that he was sore in both front legs, more so on the right, and that he responded to nerve blocks of both front feet. He also had proximal suspensory desmopathy (PSD) in both hind legs. Sue's recommendation was to investigate further the cause of pain in the front feet, to determine whether it was worth treating the hind legs."

Jonny had a magnetic resonance imaging (MRI) scan of both front feet, which showed a few bony changes but no soft tissue concerns. The hypothesis was that the front limbs were being over-loaded because of the pain behind. Jonny underwent surgery, bilateral neurectomy and fasciotomy, to resolve the pain from the hindlimb proximal suspensory desmopathy. The surgery involved removing a piece of the nerve that provides principal innervation to the suspensory ligament and cutting the band of tissue (fascia) that compresses the ligament in a compartment formed by the cannon bone and splint bones and the fascia.

Jonny's rehabilitation went well and included dynamic mobilisation exercises, walking exercise and using body bands. However, when Thea got back on Jonny was still unbalanced walking downhill. "He was trying to go laterally, and we realised that the pain in the front feet was still significant. He had his front legs investigated again, after four months of rehabilitation. Following this investigation, Jonny had remedial farriery, including pads on his front feet and both his fetlock joints were medicated. I had gait analysis done to help get the farriery work right and I started feeding a joint supplement recommended by my vet.

"Jonny is now doing better than he has for a year. He's long-reined, is going to a water treadmill (which has made a significant difference to his walk), and does baited stretches, all as 'normal'. He has physiotherapy checks every three months, and his regular vet, who is doing his follow-up, is pleased with his top-line development and his core strength. When I jumped him again for the first time he felt fantastic and he's loading into the lorry willingly.

"I may not be able to do as much as I thought with him, but I should be able to do a reasonable amount. I know him so well now, and I feel that I'm really listening to him. He's stopped stumbling and tilting at the poll. Although he will occasionally 'lose' his right hindlimb in his ridden work, he's stopped kicking out when I pick up the right hindlimb and is no problem for the farrier. I'm hoping to get back to low level dressage and jumping, or whatever is appropriate for Jonny."

LET'S START WITH SOME QUESTIONS:

1. *How good are you at recognising lameness?*
2. *Which professionals are part of the team supporting your horse?*
3. *Which professionals do you have supporting your own musculoskeletal health?*
4. *Are there other professionals you'd like to have on board, either for yourself or your horse?*
5. *Whose advice do you trust most, in relation to your horse?*

ASK THE EXPERTS

Who Is On Your Team?

In Sue Palmer's book, 'Understanding Horse Performance: Brain, Pain or Training?', there were two key themes that came through strongly from the twenty-seven guest contributors, which included many eminent equestrian professionals. The first theme was to first check for pain, before assuming that a problem was due to behaviour. The second was to have a good team working with your horse. Choose a team of knowledgeable, experienced, qualified professionals whom you trust and respect. Maintain a close relationship with this team, asking questions and developing your own knowledge and experience along the way.

With this in mind, we wanted to share with you the viewpoint of knowledgeable, experienced, qualified practitioners in many of the areas that you might look for support with your horse. We asked these professionals some questions around their work, and in particular around pain in ridden horses. They have each replied in their individual way. We hope that you find their insights helpful and inspiring.

Many of these professionals have a website where you can find out more about their specialism. At the end of the chapter, we have included a list of websites where you can find practitioners in the United Kingdom, in the areas of professionalism where there is a national association or regulatory body. Some similar bodies exist in other countries as well.

Veterinary medicine

- *Dr Jessica Kidd*

BA, DVM, CertES (Orth), Diplomate ECVS, MRCVS, RCVS and European Recognised Specialist in Equine Surgery
www.kiddvet.com

"What do you love most about your work?"

I am an equine vet and a specialist equine surgeon by training. I love many things about my work. A few of the top things are the privilege of spending all day with horses, trying to help them through their veterinary and surgical issues, and working to improve the quality of their lives. Horses in pain don't always show us tell-tale signs such as a severe lameness, and it's easy to underestimate the debilitating nature of chronic pain. When I discuss poor performance and pain-related issues with owners, I always say to them that the bottom line is if they think that something is amiss with their horse, just have the horse examined by a professional because one of two things will happen: either the veterinary surgeon will say "I've identified a few things which may be an issue which we should look into" or the vet might say "I can't find anything amiss, and we've had a good look so continue on, and then you have a clear conscience that you're not compounding any issues".

"Tell the reader about a horse you have worked with, which was apparently sound but was showing signs of pain in ridden work. How did you help the horse? What was the outcome?"

I remember clearly a horse that belonged to two friends of mine, a mother, and a daughter. The first time I saw ex-racehorse Red, he was about 17-years-old. His owners adored him but said that he was "quirky" and had retired from racing for always being crabby and in a bad mood. They asked if I would have a look to see if there might be an explanation. In fairness to them, they had requested input from others previously, but nothing was identified. The long and the short of it was that Red had impinging spinous processes or "kissing spines" as we call them. I diagnosed this through a combination of a physical and orthopaedic examination, back radiographs, but most importantly a local anaesthetic block of the suspicious areas of his back. This transformed Red, although in this instance only for the two hours that the local anaesthetic was effective. With his back blocked he was able to trot and canter normally, and apparently comfortably, and just seemed so relaxed in himself when ridden. Seventeen years of age to me is not an old horse, but many people would say that doing back surgery in a horse at that age is not justified. I have to say I can't agree with that because that would be like someone saying that your grandmother can't have a hip replacement because she's too old. Your grandmother is not going to run in the Olympics, but your grandmother wants a healthy and pain-free life, and the same holds true for horses. In the end, we did surgery on Red's back. The owners reported that in the years that they had owned him, he had never seemed so relaxed, to the point that he almost looked sleepy. They were so pleased for their horse that major pain had been alleviated.

"What piece of knowledge / advice / education do you share most regularly with your clients?"

The horses can't tell us how much things hurt. We have to use other skills to try to understand this, but I remember one of the first horses on which I had done back surgery. Although back surgery in horses is a major orthopaedic undertaking, the day after surgery the horse had an entirely different and much happier personality. I've seen this time in and time out. It says to me that the pain of the surgery that they undergo is actually outweighed by the pain with which they have been living. In a way, it is rather heart breaking to think what horses are suffering because they can't tell us, and because many people don't think to look. But the more people know to look for these things and ask for professional opinions, the better it will be for the horses.

Farriery

• *Mark Aikens*

DipWCF FdSc BSc (Hons)
Trinity Farrier Services Ltd
www.trinityfarrier.com

"What do you most like about your work?"

I love effecting objective change through farriery. Visually, this can be very pleasing when trimming or shoeing a horse that may not have been attended to regularly, and its feet have become distorted and imbalanced. I also love collaborating with a veterinarian to ameliorate lameness. This may be catastrophic in a case of laminitis, or simply improving performance by improving limb loading during the stance phase when shoe fit and an appropriate trim improves biomechanics of the lower limb.

"How do you think that your work as a farrier has improved equine welfare?"

Asymmetry of the hoof and / or the distal limb is observed when comparing the shape and angles of the hoof between contralateral limbs. This can be defined as "uneven". Whether this is genetic or occurred through injury, it can influence soundness and function, particularly in those horses ridden in an athletic discipline. I've experienced horses that appear sound when trotted in a straight line yet have struggled when working on one rein or performing a specific movement. Often the horse will change its lead leg, buck, swish its tail or shake its head to display discomfort. Shoe fit and placement and the use of pads in conjunction with foot packing may improve performance or an undiagnosed lameness and therefore improve equine welfare, but it's imperative the farrier has in-depth knowledge of anatomy and biomechanics of the foot.

"What piece of knowledge / advice / education do you share most regularly with your clients?"

Managing the environment which mostly influences the horses' feet is definitely my almost daily mantra to my clients. Hooves are critically affected by either a lack or excess of moisture, which will alter the natural function of the hoof capsule and can be detrimental to the internal structures which the hoof is there to protect. High moisture content (water, urine, mud, faeces, wet bedding) will soften the horn tubules. This results in stress and distortion of the foot, particularly the toe and heels, flattening of the sole, and changing the form of the digital cushion. At the same time, it increases the likelihood of premature shoe loss, not to mention the prevalence of thrush and white line disease. Low moisture content (wood shavings bedding, mud drying overnight on the hoof wall, sandy paddocks, overuse of some topical hoof treatment) will decrease the lipid content of the horn. This can result in cracks in the horn, retained sole and can limit normal hoof mechanics by reducing the pliability of the hoof capsule and the role this performs in healthy blood flow to the foot and shock absorption.

Saddlery

- *Ellie Tomlinson*

Master Saddler & Society of Master Saddlers Qualified Saddle Fitter
www.medidasaddles.co.uk

"What do you love most about your work?"

As a saddle fitter, I see many horses that are subjected to a degree of discomfort, due to the fit of their saddle or use of inappropriate equipment. This is often down to a misinformed, well-intentioned owner. It can typically be a simple fix that makes a world of difference to a horse's happiness and complete health. If one owner mounts their horse and immediately says 'wow that feels better, you don't notice how wrong something is until it is right', or if I see the horse take a deep breath and relax for the first time in our session once the saddle has been correctly balanced, then I go home happy that day.

As eyes on the ground for many owners, I can provide an alternative interpretation of the horse and their attitude to their work. This is an interpretation that is not always easily accessed by riders onboard, if they do not have a regular and consistent trainer. I can spot changes in a horse from one appointment to the next, which may be due to pain having been introduced at some point along the way.

"Tell the reader about a horse you have worked with, which was apparently sound but was showing signs of pain in ridden work. How did you help the horse? What was the outcome?"

I was recently invited by a new client to assess the suitability of a saddle purchased from a different supplier. The client had concerns regarding the fit. She had noted a deterioration in the horse's general demeanour and then overall health, after the introduction of this saddle. The horse was initially still amenable to be being ridden and worked but was getting less so. I was instructed to give a second opinion after the client's concerns were disregarded by the initial supplier. Coming from a fresh perspective and a different background of experiences, my opinion was that the saddle was incorrectly flocked and balanced, and as such, was causing the horse some pain and despondency. We experimented with different saddles, girths, and saddle pads, with some success but still not 100%. We reached a point where I couldn't do any more within my professional context, and I pressed the owner to initiate some veterinary investigations. It transpired that the original ill-fitting saddle had most likely caused enough pain and associated anxiety to trigger the onset of hind gut ulcers. There were no other changes in the horse's environment or routine that could be attributed to this diagnosis. After some time off and correct medication, we reintroduced the horse to ridden work with different equipment set up and paid close attention to any reactions the horse had along the way. This horse is now back to full fitness with a happy owner.

"What piece of knowledge / advice / education do you share most regularly with your clients?"

The advice that I regularly roll out in response to situations such as this is, as an owner, trust your gut instinct. If you think there is something amiss with your horse or your set-up in some way then do investigate, even if it means getting a second opinion, in addition to that of your original professional.

Physiotherapy

- *Sonya Nightingale*

MCSP
Past Chairperson of the Association of Chartered Physiotherapists in Animal Therapy,
Past President of the Register of Animal Musculoskeletal Practitioners
www.highworth-physio.co.uk

"What do you love most about your work?"

I have always had a fascination for anatomy and how it influences the gait and function of an animal. How very slight variances in angle, dimension, and weight can both positively and negatively affect the ability of an animal to move economically, to perform to a high level, to stay sound, and even to continue working over a prolonged lifespan. Being able to use this knowledge, to analyse the animal in front of you, and to then observe and potentially help with any anomalies allowing improved and prolonged pain-free function, is a highly rewarding process. Teaching the owners and carers of these animals about the creatures in their care, and what to watch out for, just cements it!

"Tell the reader about a horse you have worked with, which was apparently sound but was showing signs of pain in ridden work. How did you help the horse? What was the outcome?"

This love of the analysis of anatomy led to me helping a horse which was listed as a potential for destruction. He is a trigeminal neuralgia head shaker. He was and is sound but had become unrideable, due to the severe head twitch, and the fact that he was face striking with his forelimbs. I was armed with the knowledge of the path of the trigeminal nerve and its functions, plus knowledge of how these conditions are treated in human medicine. I treated him, with veterinary consent, using modalities that hadn't been used in this way on horses before to our knowledge. Suffice it to say that he is now completely rideable and competing successfully at medium level dressage, albeit with management strategies in place. Head shaking is often not recognised as something that is painful. It is, and these animals need help. (Authors' comment: Although headshaking can be managed in some horses, for example by use of a nose net or electrical stimulation, others are currently refractory to all methods of treatment. Horses which are head shakers should be differentiated from those which are head tossers; horses with repetitive head tossing usually have musculoskeletal pain.)

"What piece of knowledge / advice / education do you share most regularly with your clients?"

My love of the musculoskeletal system and how it functions also leads me to one of my pet hates, and that is the overuse of bandages and wraps on horses' limbs. The matchy-matchy craze has driven this forward in numerous instances. Research has clearly shown us that uncovered equine limbs frequently work at close to the maximum safe temperature to avoid soft tissue destruction. Why would you then cover the limb and risk heating it further? Protection is sometimes required when an animal is working but, if it isn't, leave the limb clear and, if it is, remove it as soon as you have finished.

Chiropractic

- *Dr Vav Simon*

DC AMC FRCC
Past President of the McTimoney
Chiropractic Association
animal group, past Director of
Academic Affairs of the Royal
College of Chiropractors
Animal Faculty

"What do you love most about your work?"

As a Doctor of Chiropractic and a veterinary chiropractor for many years, I have witnessed trends change in the equine world. It is now easy to keep a horse, either at livery or in a small pony paddock. Many people now fulfil their childhood dream to own one. While all the horses I see are loved, not all can do the jobs they are purchased for. This can lead to problems for the horse through behaviour or injury. As a result, I spend a lot of time educating owners about exercise regimes, feeding, fitness and work. I love helping owners to get the best from their animal, and the variety of horses I see makes work interesting.

"Tell the reader about a horse you have worked with, which was apparently sound but was showing signs of pain in ridden work. How did you help the horse? What was the outcome?"

One case I remember was when I was working with a professional trainer. Being of the old school, she always wanted her charges checked for muscle balance and skeletal symmetry before starting a training programme. A Highland horse had come in to be produced for showing, as he had been bucking his owner off, and was clearly uncomfortable in his work. He was a willing horse, so it was out of character when he began to buck and twist when anyone sat deep in the saddle. His saddles, both working and show, were checked and found to be a perfect fit. So, I was asked to check his back, since he was sound, his action was beautiful, and the vet could not find any problem in his gait.

When I palpated his back, I found subluxation in his thoracic spine, an area not usually affected in this way. It turned out that his owner was disabled and had to sit in a very one-sided way to accommodate her previously broken pelvis and hip injury. I treated him with the McTimoney Chiropractic method of adjustment and then soft tissue treatment. After appropriate rest, he started to work beautifully for the trainer.

To prevent the issue recurring, I then treated his owner, who had not had treatment since her radical surgery for the pelvic injury. The chiropractic intervention helped the dynamic interaction between the horse and the rider to improve. The rider's position changed, which distributed her weight evenly, and it also gave her more comfort when walking.

(Authors' comment: The term 'subluxation' is used differently by different professions. The consensus definition of the Association of Chiropractic Colleges is 'Subluxation is a complex of functional and / or structural and / or pathological articular changes that compromise neural integrity and may influence organ system function and general health'. When used by a veterinarian it implies gross partial malalignment of a joint.)

Osteopathy

- *Eleanor Andrews*

M.Ost, D.O. Animal Osteopathy, PGCertHE, PG Cert. Paediatric Osteopathy
www.animalosteopathy
international.com

"What do you love most about your work?"

Working for the betterment of animal welfare and quality of life, on behalf of the profession, as a lecturer and as an individual practitioner. I love working with complex cases which are multifaceted, and there is nothing more rewarding than working as part of a team to bring an animal back to optimal health and function and teaching others how to achieve this.

"Tell the reader about a horse you have worked with, which was apparently sound but was showing signs of pain in ridden work. How did you help the horse? What was the outcome?"

I worked with an 8-year-old show jumper with reduced performance. Osteopathic assessment used a full-body assessment approach to support focused veterinary intervention for bilateral mild arthritis of the hocks, likely predisposed by previous developmental joint issues (osteochondritis dissecans) and being worked "too hard too young". Targeted veterinary intervention was undertaken, and an osteopathic intervention initiated alongside remedial farriery, addressing hoof balance, and providing supportive shoeing.

Osteopathic intervention involved working locally on the suboptimal hock function and globally on the compensatory mechanisms which had led to increased concussive forces through the forelimbs, resulting in discomfort and altered performance.

Rehabilitation aimed to replace suboptimal biomechanics with improved, balanced movement supported by correct muscle function and led to the horse working as a fluid unit, making movement look effortless. This required owner dedication and coordinated osteopathic and trainer communications. However, the horse responded well to intervention and post rehabilitation horse and rider are enjoying competing once more.

"What piece of knowledge / advice / education do you share most regularly with your clients?"

We cannot treat a horse as a human or anthropomorphise them. As prey animals, naturally, they will flee first or fight if unable. Remember, we control all aspects of the horse's external environment, which in turn shapes their internal environment. Horses perceive the world and think and process stimuli differently to humans. Horses are not naughty – rather, respond to the environment they are in. For example, if they do not understand your wishes/aids or are in pain, they will elicit a response due to this confusion or discomfort. Horses follow the path of the least resistance and cannot verbalise the problem. Thus, we must seek the cause of behavioural responses or changes and be the horse's advocate, looking for the reason for their response rather than berating them for showing natural behaviours in the unnatural world we place them in. A horse is an athlete, they undertake exercise often with a rider on board, and just as a human athlete is supported by a team of professionals, your horse should be too.

Dentistry

- *Grant Chanter*

EDT
Past Chairman of the British Association of Equine Dental Technicians; served for four years with The King's Troop Royal Horse Artillery reaching the rank of Captain; awarded The Royal Warrant to Her Majesty The Queen for Equine Dental and Bitting Services
www.grantchanterequinedentist.co.uk

"What do you love most about your work?"

What I still love, after 23 years as an equine dental technician, is the reward of spending time with a horse that trusts you enough to carry out quite invasive procedures while also making a positive difference to the long-term welfare of that animal.

"Tell the reader about a horse you have worked with, which was apparently sound but was showing signs of pain in ridden work. How did you help the horse? What was the outcome?"

Horses react to pain in different ways and to different degrees of evasion in my experience. Some horses can have the sharpest teeth, or quite acute bitting trauma but show no visible signs of pain. Whereas some very sensitive horses can have the slightest edge to a tooth or pinch from a bit and it is enough for them to run off from the discomfort. One example was a Para-Olympic horse that was showing a head tilt when ridden. A team, including a physiotherapist, farrier, saddle fitter and veterinarian could not find a reason for it. As a last ditch measure the yard manager asked me to check the horse and I duly gave the horse a routine dental treatment. The horse had some relatively minor sharp enamel points on one side which proved to be the cause of the head tilt. We now treat this horse every six months, knowing that this horse is extra sensitive. Another example is a horse of my own that ran away from the contact when I was warming up for a dressage test. On inspecting his mouth, I found the smallest of pinches to the corner of his mouth from the loose ring snaffle. I changed the bit to a standard eggbutt snaffle and he went back to his normal self."

"What piece of knowledge / advice / education do you share most regularly with your clients?"

The advice I give most regularly to clients is to get the teeth checked regularly, by a properly trained equine dental technician, as per our advice, and to check the horse's mouth regularly after riding for any signs of bitting sores. As horse owners we regularly check the horse's legs and hooves for lumps, bumps etc., but we seem to forget about the mouth as it is out of sight so out of mind! I feel the equestrian world as a whole does not put enough importance or priority into the horse's mouth, considering how important is the clear communication from the rider's hand to the horse's mouth!

Nutrition

- *Clare MacLeod*

MSc RNutr
Independent Registered Equine
Nutritionist
www.equinenutritionist.com

"What do you love most about your work?"

As an equine nutritionist, what I love most about my work is helping owners to find their way through the myriad of products available to feed their horse, and to have peace of mind about their horse's diet and feeding management. As a happy consequence, this delivers good health and welfare to the horse, which is what I also love about my work. I think that an owner's peace of mind goes a long way to help make their horse's life happier.

"Tell the reader about a horse you have worked with, which was apparently sound but was showing signs of pain in ridden work. How did you help the horse? What was the outcome?"

Two horses I've worked with showed symptoms of discomfort and excessive anxiety, which the owners were hoping to relieve via the diet. In both cases, I recommended that the owner discuss options with their vet, including investigating stomach health. Both horses had stomach ulcers, which were treated with medication and as a result the horses had relief and their discomfort was removed. Both were also recommended diets to support good digestive tract health. A happy athlete relies entirely on their human carer to provide a well-balanced diet, meaning one that provides all the essential nutrients they need daily. I'd add to that definition by stating it must also fulfil the behavioural needs of the horse. A balanced diet includes adequate energy (calories), protein, fibre, vitamins and minerals, enough clean fresh water, and controlled intake of non-structural carbohydrates (NSC). The latter is dependent on the horse's health status, body composition (fat content) and exercise regime. A balanced diet is an important foundation to get right before therapeutic supplements are added.

"What piece of knowledge / advice / education do you share most regularly with your clients?"

The piece of advice I share most regularly with my clients is to think for themselves, trust their instincts, and monitor their horse regularly. To consider their individual horse, think carefully about what options are available, educate themselves, invite only the opinions of experts into their decisions, and then have faith in that process. There's a lot of noise to overcome nowadays, when making decisions on how to look after and feed your horse, so you need to have a clear route through those distractions.

Horsemanship

- *Kelly Marks*

Founder of Intelligent Horsemanship
Specialising in horsemanship skills and communication between horse and human
www.intelligenthorsemanship.co.uk

"What do you love most about your work?"

I love seeing how seemingly simple things can make massive changes to the horse human relationship, both on the ground and when ridden. The sooner the human takes responsibility for what's happening, as in 'now what can I do differently to make this work' the sooner we get great results. I'm of the opinion that nowadays we can provide a much better life for horses in a domestic environment than they would have in the wild. Having observed and interacted with a feral herd in Namibia, the original single, scarred 'old' horse I came across turned out to be 5-years-old. Nature isn't kind to the weak. Whether riding is good for the horse or rider depends, like many things, on 'how it's done'. We know as humans that reasonable exercising and weight training helps keep us 'young' for longer. 'Reasonable' being the optimum word. A horse can only go on so long racing or in a dressage or showjumping arena, but they may have another ten years or more of quality life with the right care and enjoyable exercise through hacking, alongside physiotherapy combined with an appropriate suppling routine.

"Tell the reader about a horse you have worked with, which was apparently sound but was showing signs of pain in ridden work. How did you help the horse? What was the outcome?"

We've always done soundness checks at our horsemanship demonstrations, and it is surprising how many seemingly sound horses (to their owner) show up lame when trotting in a circle. A quite dramatic example though was when I was approached about a pony once which 'was good cross-country but very grumpy in the arena'. There were tiny white dots on her back where her hair had gone white. I looked at her saddle with a colleague, we could see that there were staples sticking out the bottom of her saddle into her back, killing the hair follicles and so creating those marks. When her adrenaline was up, it could override the pain to some extent, but no wonder she was grumpy in the arena!

"What piece of knowledge / advice / education do you share most regularly with your clients?"

The equestrian world is good at instructing students how to get their horses to do things. Where Intelligent Horsemanship attempts to fill a gap is educating students to recognise that the horse needs a voice as well. If we learn to observe carefully, horses can really help us to understand their needs. Dr Sue Dyson's excellent pain ethogram is a great example of helping the uninitiated to see that those faces being pulled and the displacement behaviours being shown – tail swishing, for example – are signs of a horse in discomfort. Those physical issues should be helped before any 'training' goes further. There are so many subtle signs from horses, but we won't see them if we don't look.

One of the biggest favours we can do our horses, once their basic needs are met, is to know ourselves and be at peace with ourselves. Horses are sensitive prey animals, and they can pick up on our emotions. If we take time to de-stress with a few breathing exercises and gratitude before we approach them, it can give them a happier life. Maybe your day has been busy, but don't treat your horse as another task to get over and done. Changing the 'busy, busy' attitude has benefits for the human, too. Don't skim through life – it's short enough already!

Riding and Training

- *Boo Riley*

Freelance Rider
www.facebook.com/
BooRileyEquine/

"What do you love most about your work?"

As a freelancing rider and instructor, I love being able to help owners build a solid, lasting relationship with their horse. The initial reason for my involvement with new clients is often to assist with a new horse which has turned out to be less experienced/schooled/mannerly (delete as appropriate!) than was thought at the time of purchase. This usually requires me to train the horse to begin with, but typically evolves into educating owners about how to handle / ride / progress their horse.

"Tell the reader about a horse you have worked with, which was apparently sound but was showing signs of pain in ridden work. How did you help the horse? What was the outcome?"

I was recently involved with a young horse which the prospective owners had on trial. I began with groundwork and noted that it was very much more reluctant to move in one direction than the other. Under saddle, the horse was lacking enthusiasm, and was very difficult to keep in front of the leg. I felt that I needed to raise these issues with my client before the horse was purchased, and as such it received a thorough vetting with x-rays, which it sadly, but unsurprisingly, failed. I can only hope that its original owners were responsible enough to investigate the issues found. (Authors' comment: A veterinarian can either recommend or not recommend a horse for purchase. They are advised not to use the terms 'pass' and 'fail' relative to a pre-purchase examination.)

"What piece of knowledge / advice / education do you share most regularly with your clients?"

I often discuss with clients the importance of addressing problems with their horses, so that as owners they learn to consider the reason for poor performance or undesirable behaviours (brain, pain, or training?). So many people believe that their horse can be naughty, and so needs punishing for that behaviour. This makes me sad, so I do my best to help as many people as I'm able to understand the reasons horses behave as they do. Where pain is concerned, I find that so many owners simply don't recognise it in their horse.

They believe that their horse is different / special / unusual and say 'he / she has always done it that way, so it's normal for him / her'. They would rather not consider that pain may be the cause.

Coaching

- *Mary Wanless*

BSc, BHSI, internationally renowned coach, author of the 'Ride With Your Mind' books
www.mary-wanless.com

A philosophical commentary on the interaction between horses and riders

Left to themselves, horses living in fields are not very creative. Some are content, others mope. A few make mischief, bossing the others around, chasing them off the best food, and damaging fences. A small percentage (and even a small percentage of good jumping horses) jump out searching for greener pastures. When a human provides the intention and inspiration that moves them beyond living like an over-grown free-range hen, many are happy to join the adventure, and to go and see the world. At the start of a working day in the barn, some bang on the stable door, appearing to (effectively) shout, "Me first!". They often have an opinion about what they want to do, and the games that humans like to play with horses can be fun for the horses too and become their raison d'être.

It thrills me when successful, well-known competition riders break the mould of tradition, and keep their horses out at grass, or at the very least provide significant time at pasture each day. To me, husbandry matters. Systems that are more horse-friendly may not look as neat and up-market as we humans think they ought to. Of course, access to more acres of land really helps, and land is hard to come by. Solariums, water treadmills, and other inventions are wonderful for elite horses or those needing rehabilitation, but the needs of the average horse are largely met by space, air, grass (with extra food as appropriate), and companions.

The needs of ridden horses go beyond this, and beyond good farriery, saddlery, dentistry and feeding. All of these are controversial fields, where many wrong assumptions have been made in the past. Recent research, and stringent observations in the field, are leading to valuable insights, pioneered in practice by profound thinkers daring to work outside a very traditional box. Both evidence-based practice, and practice-based evidence, are combining to transform horse care and riding.

Inevitably, some horses are more robust and capable than others, and sadly many slightly lame horses are not perceived as lame. Even those which do not limp can have compromised bodies. They are the 'walking wounded', soldiering on regardless. How many humans do you know who are compromised by aches and pains, without actually limping? These horses need a sensitive rider who is willing to spend money, and / or give them a less demanding job.

About 20% of horses, along with around 20% of us humans, are more sensitive than the other 80%. Many chestnut mares come in this category. Some horses care about how we ride them much more than others, and the better we ride them, the more discerning they become. We are showing them what the ideal rider-horse partnership feels like, and amplifying their perception of the lack of skill in others.

Riding has its ethics, which become more important when the challenges are high, and / or when the horse's adrenaline cannot inoculate him against our ignorance or ineptness. This leaves the horse world debating which horse sports are more or less horse-friendly, but whatever the answer to that conundrum, most riders will agree that the days of brute force and ignorance are behind us. They need to be behind us for the public to maintain our social licence to operate. Within this, we have to resist the biggest modern-day temptation: to want higher performance (and hence a more valuable horse) *now*. Money talks way too loudly for many horses' good.

When the way you look at things changes, what you see changes too, and you find more of what there is to see. My personal contribution to horse welfare (and that of the 'Ride With Your Mind' coaches I have trained) revolves around how we ride them, and what we can potentially learn to feel. Horses are born able to 'read' us riders, but we have to go on a profound training course to learn how to 'read' them. This requires us to take more responsibility, especially given that the horse is the ideal scapegoat for poor performance (more easily blamed than your tennis racquet or running shoes).

My approach is based on a deep appreciation that horses *cannot not know* if we riders are supporting our body weight well or are riding 'like a sack of potatoes'; if our centre of mass is ahead or behind theirs; if we are sitting off to one side; if we are wiggly and jiggly or 'shovey' and resorting to kick-and-pull. When we can stabilise ourselves well on the forces of their movement, without becoming disorganised by those forces, they do not have to contort or defend themselves. To a ridden horse this matters, and it adds to the way that work, as well as good husbandry, can enhance his life.

LET'S OPEN THIS UP TO A WIDER PERSPECTIVE: TALKING POINTS

1. *Do you know which organisations, associations, or governing bodies the professionals who work with your horse are registered with?*
2. *Do you question and research the science behind the marketing claims of the products you use with your horse?*
3. *Should regular lessons, veterinary checks, farriery, physiotherapy, saddle fit, dental check and / or nutritional advice be made compulsory?*

CASE STUDY: **RICKY**
By Heidi Hunter-Cope

"I wish that I'd listened to what Ricky was trying to say."

Ricky and Heidi Hunter-Cope

Ricky is a 16hh Thoroughbred gelding, a rising 14-years-old ex-racehorse. He hurdled until he was 5-years-old but wasn't overly fast. The race-trainer's daughter evented Ricky for several years before Heidi bought him aged 10 for dressage, showjumping and eventing at riding club level.

"Ricky has always had a few 'funny' behaviours, which I put down to coming off a race yard," said Heidi. "He throws his head around in the stable, gurns and pulls funny faces. In September 2020 he started being a bit girthy, so I called the vet, the saddle fitter and the physiotherapist."

Gastric ulcers were found and treated, and Ricky came back into full work a couple of months later. But there were still niggles. "He would pull faces, go disunited sometimes, or change legs just before a fence, and was also less forward off the leg. We went cross-country schooling and Ricky reared and napped. Not long after, we went to a show-jumping competition and he jumped beautifully, although I felt something strange in the way he was going halfway around the course. The same thing happened in a lesson the next week, but the instructor couldn't see anything. I had another lesson the next week, and two days later he was really lame behind. I was aware of the Ridden Horse Pain Ethogram and wondered, if I videoed him, how many of the behaviours I would see."

The local vet performed some nerve blocks, but no improvements were seen. The sacroiliac region was medicated but there was no change in Ricky's performance. However, failure of a horse to respond to medication of the sacroiliac joint region does not preclude the presence of lumbosacroiliac joint region pain. At this point, Heidi contacted Sue Dyson. After a day spent working with Ricky, Sue diagnosed proximal suspensory desmopathy in both hindlimbs, as well as chronic laminitis in both front feet, likely trauma rather than diet-related, and a substantial component of lumbosacroiliac region pain. The saddle also contributed to discomfort.

"With the benefit of hindsight, I can recognise various behaviours leading up to this point and wish

Ricky and Heidi Hunter-Cope

that I'd listened to what Ricky was trying to say. Sue didn't feel that Ricky would be able to do the eventing that I had hoped for, but she felt that he could hack several times a week. She was happy for him to go into rehabilitation, but the laminitis needed to settle first. Ricky had always been very sensitive in front, uncomfortable on uneven ground and stones. I had assumed it was just because of sensitive soles."

After eight months off due to recurring laminitis, and plenty of remedial farriery, Ricky was brought back into work. The process involved long-reining, raised poles and regular visits to the water treadmill.

"Ricky now has a treeless Smart saddle and he steps out a lot better in this one. The physiotherapist treats him every six weeks and he felt great when I got back on. He's much lighter off the leg and feels elastic in the hand," says Heidi. "I tried a couple of sessions of schooling, but on the third session, some of his old behaviours showed up straight away. He went back to long-reining, then hacking, and all the problem behaviours have gone again.

"It's fascinating to look back and watch videos. We did an online dressage test two weeks before he went lame, and knowing what I know now, I can see a very subtle lameness and behaviours from the RHpE. I plan to get into the habit of applying the RHpE via video recording once a month with the help of a friend – it's hard to recognise if a horse becomes abnormal when you ride them every day. I prefer to video the horse's performance and then apply the ethogram to the video recording of the horse because I can go back over it – I'm not good enough to spot all the behaviours in the moment."

Unless you are using the RHpE regularly (daily) it will not become second nature to apply or necessarily easy to apply in real time. The use of good quality video footage viewed on a tablet or laptop computer is strongly advocated.

RELEVANT WEBSITES FOR THE UNITED KINGDOM (MANY OTHER COUNTRIES HAVE SIMILAR ORGANISATIONS)

Veterinary medicine: www.findavet.rcvs.org.uk
British Equine Veterinary Association: www.beva.org.uk
Farriery: www.wcf.org.uk
Dentistry: www.baedt.com
Saddlery: www.mastersaddlers.co.uk
Physiotherapy: www.acpat.org

Chiropractic: www.mctimoneyanimal.co.uk
Osteopathy: www.associationofanimalosteopaths.com
Register of Animal Musculoskeletal Practitioners: www.rampregister.org
Coaching: www.bhs.org.uk

CHAPTER 6

What If My Horse Is In Pain?

"The history of mankind is carried on the back of a horse."
Author Unknown

CASE STUDY: **SAM**
By Anne Bondi

Anne Bondi and Sam

"For the first time, I heard him grind his teeth, just once. I was aware it meant he was struggling to do what I was asking."

"I bought Sam as a 6-year-old, with consistently good jumping form at 1 metre level, as a future event prospect. He was recommended for purchase based on a five-stage pre-purchase veterinary examination with a full set of radiographs. As a big, immature Irish Sports Horse, he looked more like a 4-year-old, but I hoped that with correct training and management he would develop strongly. Although he had a naturally big, ultra-careful jump, he never really felt forward going enough on the flat. Again, I hoped that this would improve as he matured and developed strength and stamina."

Sam's training progressed well, but after about six months, Anne felt that he had plateaued. "Canter right had improved immeasurably and was now balanced and engaged, but canter left was not as good, and the difference was now more noticeable because of the overall improvement in his work. The right hindlimb felt jarring in trot and canter on the left rein. He always wanted to come above the bit in the trot to left canter transition. There was a slight tendency for the left canter to become four-time, so I felt it was time to see if there were any problems brewing that might be compromising his continued development."

A veterinary review report stated that there was very mild asymmetry of the pelvic musculature. No lameness was detectable moving in hand, on the lunge or after flexion tests. However, the canter was rather laboured, lacking 'jump', and the saddle tended to slip to the right on the left rein. Saddle slip may occur because of asymmetry of the horse's back, asymmetry of flocking of the saddle or rider crookedness, but hindlimb lameness is the most common cause. Saddle slip may induce rider crookedness and may result in asymmetrical compression of the saddle flocking.

Nerve blocking of the right tarsometatarsal (hock) joint reduced the saddle slip significantly, and Sam became more manoeuvrable and symmetrical within the paces. His hock joint was therefore medicated with hyaluronan and a corticosteroid. "There was a significant difference in Sam's work. He felt more forward and symmetrical, especially in canter, which improved enormously in its engagement. He gained consistent British Eventing wins and placings.

"However, after three months, the left canter once again started to feel four-time and the saddle was leaving an asymmetric rub on Sam's back." Another review found that there was now a subtle right hindlimb toe drag and, because treatment had been successful before, the right hock was medicated again.

A pattern emerged: for three months after medication, there was a substantial improvement and Sam's competitive outings were successful, but at the end of each period there was a subtle deterioration in his work, especially in canter. Both canters would start to feel 'flat'. Sam would open his mouth at times in canter left, the rein contact would become less steady, and he would oscillate his head slightly from side to side. Another review found a positive right hindlimb flexion test and a notable decrease in the suspension phase in both canters. Further nerve blocking to the sacroiliac joints resulted in substantial improvement. Therefore, the sacroiliac joints were medicated in addition to the right hock.

"The pattern continued: after medication, the work improved enormously, and Sam was really developing in strength. He was demonstrably happier, starting to come out of himself and, a year after his arrival, he at last started to interact with me as 'his' person. He continued to event consistently well and qualified several times for the Grassroots Championships. He was now working towards Prix St Georges level on the flat, and his jumping was gaining a power that I have seldom felt in any horse.

"A slight deterioration in the contact was the first sign that something was again troubling Sam, and for the first time, I heard him grind his teeth, just once. I was aware it meant he was struggling to do what I was asking.

Anne Bondi and Cas

"As the training progressed the subtle signs of discomfort would appear in different ways: holding his tail slightly to the left; a loss of rhythm in canter half-pass left; a tail swish in canter pirouette to the left; becoming mildly over-bent in 10 m diameter circles to the left. For the first time, Sam started to rush his fences or occasionally knock a pole."

Another review showed mild bilateral hindlimb lameness, which resolved with nerve blocks just below the hocks. An ultrasound scan confirmed mild proximal suspensory desmopathy. It was decided that neurectomy of the deep branch of the lateral plantar nerve would give Sam the best possible chance of returning comfortably to full work.

After successful surgery and a comprehensive rehabilitation programme, Sam's return to work was excellent. Regular veterinary reviews and sacroiliac joint medication as necessary allowed him to continue to develop symmetrical, powerful musculature and achieve his real potential as a jumper. Sam continued to gain power and progressed impressively in show jumping to win consistently at international 1.45 m level.

LET'S START WITH SOME QUESTIONS:

1. *What can you do if your horse has a Ridden Horse Pain Ethogram (RHpE) score of eight or more?*
2. *Is it ever ok to push your horse on through discomfort?*
3. *Would fear of the unknown affect your willingness to investigate pain in your horse?*
4. *How do you know when it's time to call the vet?*
5. *How do you choose between calling your friend, the vet, the physiotherapist, the farrier, the saddle fitter, or your instructor?*

WHAT IF MY HORSE IS IN PAIN?

What can you do next?

What can you do if you decide that your horse is uncomfortable? If you've used the Ridden Horse Pain Ethogram, and the total score is eight or more out of 24? Or if you would like to look into the horse's behaviour in more detail? What options are available to you?

Getting the right help

We understand and recognise that this process can be frustrating and confusing, especially if you have already discussed the issue and feel that it has been dismissed as irrelevant, or even non-existent. Our recommendation, in most cases, is to take your horse for a lameness investigation (otherwise known as a lameness work-up) with a veterinarian who regularly sees horses ridden and ideally includes the use of the Ridden Horse Pain Ethogram (RHpE) as part of the process. This applies whether you are a leisure rider hacking out once a week, or you are competing regularly.

Pain does not always include lameness

Musculoskeletal pain does not always include lameness that is detectable in hand or on the lunge, which is why it is so important to include ridden exercise as part of the investigation. If lameness is recognised as part of the problem, the level of lameness can vary widely, from so subtle it can barely be seen, to an obvious head nod or limp. Subtle lameness is less easily recognised and may be more difficult to get to the bottom of, especially if more than one limb is involved, compared with an obvious unilateral lameness. Don't be surprised if your veterinarian points out a low-level lameness that neither you nor your team had recognised. This is very common, especially if it is hindlimb lameness, or if it involves both forelimbs or both hindlimbs. Remember that part of the veterinarian's job is to spot lameness, it's what she or he does day in, day out. It would be unrealistic to expect yourself to have the same level of expertise in this area. If you work as a receptionist, for example, you would not expect your veterinarian to be able to work the diary system in your office. Similarly, if you are a lawyer, you would not expect your veterinarian to understand the intricacies of the law. Your veterinarian is an expert in the area of equine health, and it's vital to develop a relationship of trust. It should be borne in mind that equine veterinarians may be generalists, like a human GP, or may have a particular interest and expertise in a specific area, such as reproduction. If you were a sportsman and sustained an injury you would probably not go to your GP. You would perhaps go to a sports medicine specialist. Ideally a horse with a problem during ridden exercise needs to be investigated by an equine veterinarian with an interest in lameness and poor performance, and with appropriate expertise. Discuss this with your veterinarian, because any veterinary investigation is potentially expensive, and you need to spend your money wisely. Try to determine whether your usual veterinarian is enthusiastic about this type of investigation, or whether they would advise referral to someone with more specialist expertise.

It would be helpful if you could gather information from your horse's team, which might for example include a physical therapist, saddlery fitter, farrier, dental technician, nutritionist, coach, rider, and trainer. If your horse is insured for veterinary fees, it is advisable to inform the insurance company that an investigation is to be carried out. Check whether or not your horse is insured for veterinary fees, if there are any exclusions on your policy, and what the upper limit is that might be claimed for investigation and treatment. If your horse is not insured, work out a budget for veterinary fees that you could reasonably afford to spend, and discuss this with your veterinarian.

There are a lot of emotions involved

Trotting in hand

We find that it is common for people to be scared of contacting a veterinarian. A common phrase is, "I would rather not find out that there's something wrong." You may well know someone who has taken their horse for investigation and spent a lot of money without resolving the problems. Financial limitations might prevent you from getting the help that your horse needs, or you may want to try another route first. We're hoping that the case studies in this book will give you some confidence that getting to the root of the problem can make all the difference for your horse.

You are more likely to

go through the process of investigation into the source of the discomfort if you have an idea what to expect. For those of us who discuss pain and lameness in horses daily, it's easy to forget that most owners have never seen a lameness 'work-up', and don't have much of an understanding of what's involved. That's why in this chapter we've provided a description of some of the things that might happen. Every horse is an individual and should be treated as such, and so this is by no means a list of criteria to be followed. It's more a discussion of some possibilities, so that if your veterinarian mentions one of them, it's not new to you. The investigation and treatment into a mild forelimb lameness for a 24-year-old horse who is hacking for an hour once a week in walk, is likely to be different to the investigation of a similar level of lameness in a 10-year-old who is aiming to compete at Badminton 5* three-day event, for example. The veterinarian must work to suit the needs of the owner and rider as well as the horse, which is one reason it's important to choose a veterinarian you feel comfortable with, and confident asking questions of.

If you are unsure whether to progress with further investigation it may be worth considering a 'bute (phenylbutazone is a non-steroidal anti-inflammatory analgesic drug) trial', to assess the effect of pain-relieving medication on your horse's performance. It is important to be aware that improvement in performance and behaviour during medication and/or deterioration in performance after stopping medication are positive indicators of the presence of pain. However, a negative response to phenylbutazone does not preclude the presence of pain, because phenylbutazone is not effective in relieving all sources of pain. This is best done in collaboration with your veterinarian. It is recommended that the horse's daily performance is recorded in the week leading up to the trial. During the seven to ten days trial the horse should receive a dose suitable for the horse's body size (4.4 mg/kg twice daily) and be maintained in normal work, while continuing to monitor performance, perhaps also by application of the RHpE. After stopping treatment continue to monitor the horse's performance for the following week, bearing in mind that even if you were not aware of improvement during treatment, deterioration in performance after treatment is a significant observation.

Asking questions

Talking of asking questions, that's one of the most critical parts of the investigation, and something that's often overlooked, in our opinion. Ideally, you will have one veterinarian allocated to you and your horse. She or he must take the time to ask you many questions, and honest and considered answers will be an important part of the process! In professional speak, it's known as 'taking a history'.

These questions could include asking when the current problem started, whether it's getting better or worse, if you know what triggered it, how severe it is and how it's affecting you and your horse, whether there has been any previous treatment relating to this particular problem, what improves it and what aggravates it, whether there has been any heat or swelling and if so when this happened, if the horse's posture has changed, if you or the farrier have noticed any problems or changes when picking up the feet, and anything else you can tell the veterinarian about what is going on. However, the questions will not only be about the current lameness or poor performance. The veterinarian could include questions around the environment that your horse lives in. They might ask about the horse's daily routine, exercise pattern and workload (type, intensity, duration), the horse's level of training, and your level of knowledge and previous experience.

It is also relevant to know when the saddle fit was last checked, if routine dental work and physical therapy are performed, nutrition, medication, supplements, and more. You might be asked how often the horse lies down, whether it rolls all the way over, if the horse experiences any difficulties in getting up and down, and whether the horse has field companions and plays with them. The veterinarian might want to know if the horse is head shy or ear shy, spooky, difficult to rug or tack up, or if it pulls back when tied up. If your horse is a mare, you could be asked if she is 'mare-ish' and the signs shown by the horse and when they occur relative to her being in season. The vet might ask about the horse's behaviour in the stable, in the field, for the farrier, and how the horse performs and behaves out hacking compared with in an arena or when competing. All of these things, and more, could be relevant to the investigation into the root cause of the problem. It is alright if you don't know the answers to all the questions, it is all part of the information gathering process.

Don't worry if you get emotional talking about your horse. This is quite natural.

Watch, listen and learn

Palpation of the back to determine muscle tone and the presence or absence of a pain response.

Most veterinary practices prefer to do in-depth lameness or poor performance assessments at their clinic, but not all have suitable riding facilities. We believe that it is important that the majority of horses are assessed ridden and are reassessed ridden after nerve blocks. Therefore, this part of the investigation has to be done somewhere where there is a suitable arena or field, and a clean safe area in which to perform nerve blocks. One advantage of performing this part of the investigation away from a clinic is that you are likely to get the full, undivided attention of the veterinarian during the assessment.

Some veterinary practices will ask you to be present for the lameness work-up, and some will ask that you drop your horse off at their clinic and pick it up later. If you are asked to drop your horse off, the vets will work with your horse throughout the day as necessary. This might be because the vet needs time between assessments, for example, to allow a nerve block to take effect. It's likely that your veterinarian will be investigating more than one horse on that day, and so may switch between horses throughout the day. This means there will be periods of time when you will be waiting. It is difficult to say how long a lameness work-up will take, because this is dependent on how easy it is to find the source(s) of the pain and to make a diagnosis of the cause(s) of pain. However, if possible, we recommend that you stay with your horse during the investigation so that you are better able to understand the process. By doing this, you can appreciate improvements in your horse's performance after nerve blocks if appropriate, ideally by riding your horse and feeling the difference. This will help you to make a more informed decision when discussing treatment and rehabilitation options with the veterinarian. In some cases, your horse will need to stay at the veterinary practice overnight, perhaps if the lameness work-up is taking a long time, or if you and your veterinarian decide that treatment should be given the next day. If this is the case, you will be given the opportunity to explain your horse's needs so that the horse can be looked after in the best way possible.

Find the source(s) of the pain

A pony being assessed on the lunge on a soft surface on the left rein. There is inwards lean of the trunk and the head and neck are turned to the outside of the circle.

It is essential to determine the source(s) of pain during the lameness work-up, if at all possible. The veterinarian will perform a clinical examination (sometimes called clinical evaluation) of your horse. The horse will be assessed standing still (static assessment), and while moving in hand (dynamic or gait assessment). During the initial static assessment, the veterinarian will visually assess the horse's conformation, posture, muscle development and symmetry, and the presence of any abnormal swellings. The horse's head, neck, back and pelvic regions and the limbs will be systematically palpated (felt) to determine the presence of abnormal muscle tightness and soreness, regions of heat, pain and swelling, restrictions or alterations in range of movement of joints, and any painful reaction to flexing, extending or rotating joints. Careful attention will be paid to the horse's foot conformation and the way in which it has been trimmed and shod.

Generally, the dynamic examination includes walking and trotting your horse in a straight line on hard ground (generally level tarmac or concrete or on a small slope). Your veterinarian may perform flexion tests. This means that a leg is held in a fully or partially bent position for up to a minute, and immediately afterwards the horse is trotted in a straight line and the presence of lameness and its severity is reassessed. This can help in determining the source of pain and if lameness may be present in more than one limb. It is likely that the horse will be lunged in both directions, in walk, trot, and canter on soft ground and in walk and trot on firm ground. Don't worry if your horse cannot do any of these things, because your veterinarian will be experienced in working around this.

The gait assessment could include quantitative gait analysis using inertial measurement technology or optical motion capture; there are a growing number of systems available for this. However, quantitative gait analysis is not essential and is not a substitute for careful clinical appraisal. Measurable asymmetry does not always equate with pain-induced lameness. Moreover, in horses with lameness in more than one limb the results are sometimes confusing.

Your veterinary practice will usually have dedicated areas for these assessments. This is one reason why it may be better to take your horse to the veterinarian's practice for a lameness work-up, rather than the vet coming to your yard, where facilities may be less than ideal. You may be asked to handle the horse yourself, or it may be that a member of staff does so, which enables you to watch the horse.

Ridden exercise as part of the assessment

A horse being assessed ridden. The horse's head is behind the vertical, the ears are erect, there is a slight head tilt and left hindlimb toe drag.

The lameness work-up should include ridden exercise if the horse is in ridden work, and if there is no good reason why it should not be ridden. This might mean you riding your horse, or the veterinarian may have their own rider who is used to explaining what they feel while riding the horse. Possibly, both of you will be asked to ride. Don't be apprehensive – remember that the veterinarian will principally be evaluating the horse, not you! It can sometimes be helpful for your veterinarian to see your horse ridden by more than one rider, because the rider's balance and position could influence the way your horse goes. If you are very nervous it may be helpful for the veterinarian to see your horse ridden by a more confident rider. It might also be necessary to change the tack, for example if your veterinarian feels that the tree points of the saddle are too tight, or there is some other problem with fit of the saddle or the bridle. The RHpE can be applied during each of these assessments, as appropriate and as needed.

A horse being assessed while jumping. The ears are back and the horse has an intense stare.

Nerve blocks

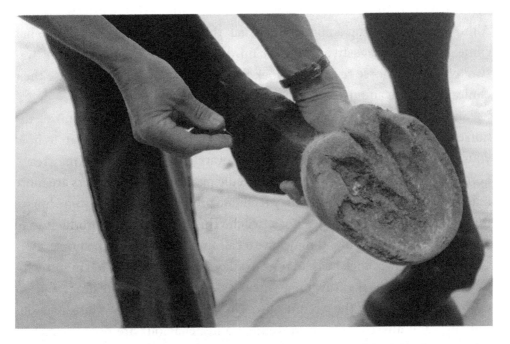

A lateral palmar nerve block being performed at the base of the lateral proximal sesamoid bone. When combined with a medial palmar nerve block this will desensitise the foot.

It is very likely that the lameness work-up will include nerve blocks (diagnostic anaesthesia) to localise the source(s) of the pain. Unless the source of the pain can be found, which usually involves nerve blocks, then it can be difficult to determine the source and cause of pain and to decide the best course of management. A nerve block involves injecting a small amount of local anaesthetic solution over nerves, which stops transmission of pain information to the brain, to desensitise (numb) a specific area of a limb. Often the veterinarian will start nerve blocking the foot and work upwards as required. Alternatively local anaesthetic solution may be injected directly into a joint (intra-articular anaesthesia) or into a region (for example, around close spinous processes). Essentially, a nerve block relieves pain in a specific area of the body, typically a region (for example, the foot or the sacroiliac region), or a joint (for example, the fetlock, or one of the hock joints). The horse is first assessed moving without nerve blocks, and the lameness grade and characteristics are noted, together with the horse's behaviour. We recommend the use of a check list for the RHpE. You will remember from earlier chapters that when the pain is removed using nerve blocks, the RHpE score goes down. Although a 'bottom up' approach is usual, this may be altered if a horse has clinical features suggestive of joint pain. For example, if a fetlock joint was swollen and the horse resented fetlock flexion, the veterinarian may use their clinical expertise and decide to block the fetlock joint first.

Successful performance of nerve blocks requires the cooperation of the horse and for safety reasons the veterinarian may ask their technician to hold your horse because the technician will be aware of how your horse may react. Some horses are extremely tolerant of needle placement while others are more reactive. Distraction with food may facilitate proceedings but for some horses it may be necessary to apply a nose twitch. This stimulates the production of endorphins in the brain and may have a calming influence on the horse.

After the nerve block has had time to take effect (after five to ten minutes for most lower limb blocks) the horse is reassessed, in hand, on the lunge and/ or ridden (depending on the circumstances in which lameness was most obvious initially), and any changes in movement and behaviour are noted. Don't be surprised if lameness deteriorates after desensitisation of a foot; this means that the foot is not a source of pain, but the horse is loading the limb more normally and accentuating pain from the injured structure. It is important that you are convinced that there is a difference in your horse's performance once the pain is removed. Don't be afraid to say if your horse still feels wrong; this means that some source of pain has been missed and your veterinarian needs to know this. Sometimes it is necessary to nerve block several areas until lameness is completely resolved, because there may be more than one source of pain in a limb contributing to lameness. It is often necessary to block more than one limb in horses which are short stepping or lacking hindlimb impulsion. This is time consuming and both you and the veterinarian must be prepared to provide this time. In some horses, nerve blocks abolish lameness in trot, but canter still feels abnormal or worse than before. This means that there is another source of pain, and if the canter is worse than before it is because the remaining source of pain has become dominant.

Of course, sometimes there is an obvious cause of pain and nerve blocks are not required or may be contra-indicated, but imaging techniques such as x-rays (radiography) or an ultrasound scan are required to determine the nature and severity of the injury. If there is a history of trauma, or sudden-onset severe lameness, or clinical signs consistent with a fracture then radiography may be the first option. Alternatively, if there is obvious enlargement of the accessory ligament of the deep digital flexor tendon (the check ligament), with associated heat and pain on palpation, then ultrasonography would be indicated.

Once the source(s) of the pain has been identified...

Once the veterinarian has decided which area(s) the pain is coming from, they may choose to use imaging tools to acquire more information and to reach a diagnosis. This is not always the case. Sometimes knowing the source of the pain alone is enough to enable you and your veterinarian to decide on the best course of action. You could decide you would rather not take things any further, for a variety of reasons. It might be that treatment is given based on the most likely diagnosis, and this in itself can act as another diagnostic tool. There may be financial constraints. Whatever route you select, it's important to remember that this route will be selected through discussion between yourself and your veterinarian. Your veterinarian will advise, and you will be guided by their knowledge and experience. However, you know your horse best, and your thoughts, feelings, and wishes are indispensable in this joint decision-making process. It is you who will be taking your horse through any rehabilitation that might be required. Your ability to achieve this, especially given the time limitations that we all suffer from, may need to be considered, as well as your long-term goals for your horse.

Diagnostic imaging

If you and your veterinarian choose to include imaging to help reach an accurate diagnosis, this imaging could include x-rays (radiography), an ultrasound scan (ultrasonography), a magnetic resonance imaging (MRI) scan, a computed tomography (CT) scan, or a bone scan (scintigraphy). Radiography and ultrasonography are used most commonly, but in some cases more in-depth imaging can be helpful. Below are very brief descriptions of each technique. It must be borne in mind with any imaging technique that an abnormality is not necessarily of clinical significance. The results must be interpreted in the light of clinical findings. For example, it is common to find radiographic evidence of osteoarthritis of a pastern (proximal interphalangeal) joint, but this often is not currently contributing to pain and lameness.

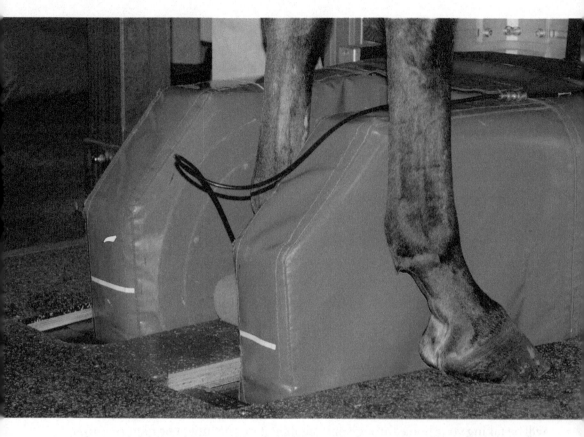

A horse's left lower limb in a low-field magnet for acquisition of magnetic resonance images of the foot.

Radiography (commonly known as x-ray) is used for imaging bones. Different tissues absorb different amounts of x-ray radiation, and this information is converted into a 2-dimensional (2-D) image. There needs to be a 40% change in bone density before abnormalities can be detected on an x-ray. X-rays provide an historical record of what has happened previously.

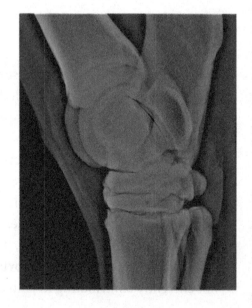

A lateromedial radiographic image of a hock. There is osteoarthritis of the centrodistal and tarsometatarsal joints.

Ultrasonography is used to assess soft tissue, such as tendons, ligaments, muscles, bone surfaces, joints, and internal organs. Ultrasound waves are projected into the body, and reflected by different structures, creating a 2-D image.

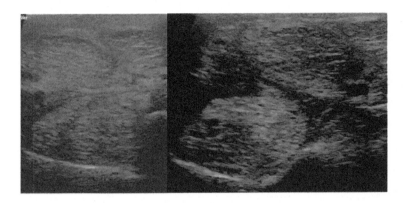

Transverse ultrasonographic images of the proximal metatarsal region of two horses with abnormalities of the suspensory ligament consistent with proximal suspensory desmopathy.

Magnetic Resonance Imaging (MRI) is used to acquire images of feet and the lower parts of the limbs (up to and including the carpus [knee] or hock) and shows both bones and soft tissues, such as tendons and ligaments.

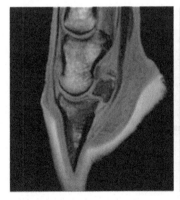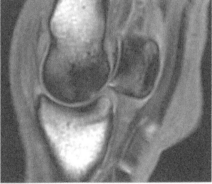

Sagittal magnetic resonance images of a foot (to the left) with reduced signal intensity in the distal phalanx and the navicular bone and a fetlock (to the right) with reduced signal intensity in the condyle of the third metacarpal bone and a focal hyperintense signal in the palmar cortex.

Computer software converts the signals from a strong magnetic field and pulsed radio waves into detailed images of thin slices of the tissues in different planes. MRI does not involve radiation. Your horse is either sedated or anaesthetised for this imaging technique, to ensure that it moves as little as possible, because movement reduces the sharpness of the image and may result in images which are not of diagnostic quality.

Nuclear Scintigraphy (commonly known as a bone scan) shows up active areas of disease within bones and sometimes soft tissues. It involves injecting a radioactive substance into the body, which is taken up by soft tissues and then bone. If there is an area of active bone change then more radioactivity is taken up. These areas show up as 'hot spots' on the image. The entire horse can be examined, or the study may be restricted to a specific region or regions. A whole-body bone scan may be very useful for a young racehorse which is performing poorly because of the high frequency of stress-related bone injuries. However, for sports horses we generally advise against whole-body bone scans. Whole-body scans are expensive, expose staff to radiation, and the results are often misleading. A bone scan is not a substitute for nerve blocks, and in many instances with low-grade lameness in sports horses the results may be negative, equivocal, or reveal 'hot spots' which are not clinically significant (i.e., are not related to the problems that you are having or the pain that your horse is experiencing). A 'hot spot' does not equate to pain causing lameness.

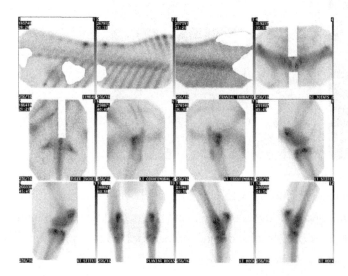

Scintigraphic (bone scan) images of the back, pelvis, hip, stifle and hock joints. There is focal intense increased radiopharmaceutical uptake (a 'hot spot') in the summit of the spinous process of the seventeenth thoracic vertebra.

Computed Tomography (commonly known as a CT scan) is a series of very thin x-ray images, using either a bone or a soft tissue algorithm. The thin slices can also be converted into 3-D reconstructions. It can give much more detailed information about bone pathology than radiography and also gives information about soft tissue lesions.

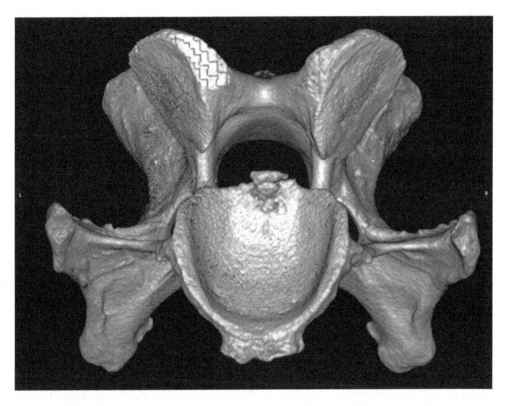

Three-dimensional reconstruction computed tomographic (CT) image of a neck vertebra. There are several osseous fragments at the top of vertebral body and new bone formation on the bottom.

Thermography is a technique to measure surface skin temperature. It does not reflect deeper temperatures. It has limited use for lameness work-ups.

Other possible investigations

Some other common investigatory procedures include blood tests, tissue biopsy, and endoscopy. In most horses these would not be part of a standard lameness investigation, although with primary muscle problems (for example, recurrent exertional myopathy, 'tying-up') measurement of muscle enzyme concentrations in the blood may be critical. Bear in mind that gastric ulcers often develop secondary to musculoskeletal pain, and it may be more logical to treat the musculoskeletal pain first and then re-evaluate the lameness / behaviour / ridden performance. This may be more cost effective and quicker than scoping the stomach, treating ulcers if needed and then reassessing performance.

It is, of course, entirely possible that your horse may have more than one problem contributing to a compromise in performance. For example, poor exercise tolerance characterised by laboured breathing or an abnormally high respiratory rate during and after exercise may reflect both pain associated with lameness and respiratory dysfunction due to equine asthma. Other problems that may be coexistent with lameness include a cardiac arrhythmia, hormonal abnormalities or gastric ulcers. We have therefore included a brief description of other diagnostic techniques below, in case these are relevant to you and your horse.

Blood samples can be collected for routine health screening, or for diagnostic purposes (for example, measurement of serum muscle enzyme concentrations before and after exercise). It may be useful to perform an oral sugar test to determine whether there is a normal response to insulin in a horse with laminitis or to test for the presence of Cushing's disease.

A **biopsy** is when a sample of tissue is extracted from the body, either using a special biopsy instrument, or cut out using a scalpel. The tissue is usually thinly sliced and special stains are used to highlight abnormalities which may be seen using a microscope (for example, a muscle biopsy if polysaccharide storage myopathy is suspected).

Endoscopy (commonly known as 'scoping') involves passing a long tube-like instrument with an in-built camera into a cavity and can be used to assess the airways and stomach, and sometimes the oesophagus and bladder.

Treatment

A 'happy' horse jumping with excellent technique

Of course, what you most want to know is what can be done to help your horse?! We hope that you now understand the importance of a detailed investigation, and how this must be tailored to the needs of both you and your horse. The priority is to find and treat the underlying cause. Assuming that a diagnosis is reached (i.e., that the root cause(s) of the problem is identified), there may be various options for treatment and management which need to be discussed. These will differ according to the structure affected. For example, are there bony changes reflecting osteoarthritis requiring medication of a joint, or is there soft tissue damage such as suspensory desmitis (inflammation of a ligament), requiring rest? The treatment and rehabilitation plan may also differ depending on what you are hoping to achieve with your horse.

Relieving the pain

A principle aim is usually to relieve pain. This might be through medication, for example, oral medicine such as phenylbutazone ('bute'), or injection into a joint, perhaps with a corticosteroid and hyaluronan. It might involve equine 'regenerative' treatments such as stem cell therapy. Your vet may recommend physiotherapy, acupuncture, or electrotherapy such as ultrasound or shockwave therapy. Treatment may require surgery. Most conditions will require a change in management. 'Management' might include a period of box rest and controlled in-hand exercise (your veterinarian and physical therapist can advise you on how best to do this), combined with exercises to maintain or increase core muscle strength, or slow ridden work, combined with changes in farriery and /or tack. Sometimes the treatment given is a 'one-off', and sometimes on-going treatment is needed. In some horses more than one treatment option is recommended. Your veterinarian will advise you on how to help your horse get back to work after the treatment (the type and intensity of ridden work), and when follow-up visits are required. The veterinarian may also want to speak with or work with your farrier, physical therapist, saddlery fitter, trainer, coach, or rider. Take the time to ask any questions that come to mind. If you have the chance, it can be a good idea to write your questions down as you're going through the day so that you can remember them when you need to. Don't feel pressurised into making immediate decisions; a few days delay is generally not going to influence the outcome.

You are at the centre

As with the entire process, treatment options will be discussed with you, and a joint decision should be made between you and your veterinarian as to the best way forward for your horse. Treatment and rehabilitation are specific to the individual. It is important to recognise that in the vast majority of cases, there are treatment options available, although there may need to be modifications in the athletic expectations for a horse. Bear in mind that repetitive work in an arena is both physically and mentally stressful for a horse; continual work on a single surface and repeated movements predispose to repetitive strain injuries. Riding on a variety of surfaces and terrains in different environments provides better mental stimuli than work confined to an arena and is likely to be beneficial for musculoskeletal health. It is important that training programmes are suitable to maximise the development of appropriate musculoskeletal strength and coordination. It may also be necessary to address the rider's position, balance and fitness to optimise the horse's chances of returning to full function. A rider who sits crookedly is likely to induce long-term changes in a horse's movement pattern and predispose to the development of pain. We believe that post-injury rehabilitation should encompass management of the horse as a whole, not just the injured structure, and a team approach is often beneficial. The extent and quality of the investigation and diagnosis are key to enabling you to make the best decision in terms of treatment and management.

TALKING POINTS

1. *Would you be confident to take your horse to the relevant professional for investigation into pain related behaviours?*
2. *Would you be able or willing to change your horse's workload if it wasn't able to continue working at the current level?*
3. *Is pain in ridden horses too readily accepted as being 'OK'?*

CASE STUDY: **RIPLEY**
By Joanne H.

"I'm relieved that I stopped trying to force him to behave; someone could have been hurt if I had kept going."

Ripley is Joanne's first horse, bought following a pre-purchase examination a few years after Joanne started riding. "I was very excited to learn how to jump. I knew I needed lots of help, so I was having regular lessons and going to clinics," said Joanne. "Ripley seemed to enjoy

Joanne H and Ripley

flatwork but was resistant to jump and pinned his ears. I was recommended to look into getting a new saddle to help both of us be more balanced."

Joanne contacted a saddle fitter, who showed her Sue Dyson's RHpE and explained how to evaluate a horse's behaviour under saddle as a display of pain, rather than simply in the context of training. However, although some of Ripley's behaviours improved with a new saddle, others did not. "Ripley would rear when going uphill, and he had a very choppy canter. He would swap leads with his hind legs in the canter or start to 'bunny hop'. He was very hard to get in front of my leg, and my trainer started using both a whip and spurs to keep him going.

"Ripley was very hard to get 'on the bit' and went with his head out in front of the vertical and tilted to one side almost all the time. We were constantly working on getting him straight because he was almost always on three tracks. Ripley also started to spook more, with a powerful spook-spin-bolt that left me scared."

The saddle fitter encouraged Joanne to consult a vet, and Ripley was diagnosed with pain in the sacroiliac joint region. He received an injection, then underwent rehabilitation, comprising box rest, hand walking and strengthening exercises.

"Ripley is now so much happier. He's easier to get forward, and I can get him on the bit now. We are starting to add in small jumps, and he is much happier about that now. The most significant change is that I can keep him in canter all the way around the arena without using my whip or spurs. He also doesn't spook as much, which makes me feel safer and more confident.

"I'm not convinced that I would have consulted a vet if I hadn't heard about the RHpE. Before my saddle fitter told me about it, I had been advised by others to send Ripley to a cowboy or sell him because the rearing scared me. Neither my trainer nor I felt we could resolve that behaviour; we both thought it was an attitude or training problem. I'm relieved that I stopped trying to force Ripley to behave; someone could have been hurt if I had kept going. Ripley is so much happier, and now, instead of being nervous to get on him, I look forward to every chance I have to ride."

SNIPPETS OF SCIENCE

"...It was concluded that the ethogram was applied consistently by veterinarians with differentiation between non-lame and most lame horses. After appropriate training in its application, the ethogram may provide a useful tool for determining the presence of musculoskeletal pain in horses performing poorly."

Dyson, S., Thomson, K., Quiney, L., Bondi, A., Ellis, A. Can veterinarians reliably apply a whole horse ridden ethogram to differentiate non-lame and lame horses based on live horse assessment of behaviour? Equine Vet. Educ. 2020, 32: 112-120. https://doi.10.1111/eve.13104.

THE BRITISH EQUINE VETERINARY ASSOCIATION (BEVA)

Contribution from Lucy Grieve MA VetMB MRCVS, Chairperson of the Ethics and Welfare Committee and a past President of BEVA, on behalf of BEVA
www.beva.org.uk

"In your opinion, how is horse riding good for a horse as well as a rider?"

Horse-riding is clearly of benefit to the rider, who seeks out the enjoyment and athleticism offered by such an activity. To understand how much the horse enjoys it is challenging, but to anyone who has watched a horse at pasture, there is evident enjoyment in the exercise they take voluntarily. Acclimatising the horse to the process and addressing tack fit, rider ability, etc. will also enable riding to be carried out with minimal stress and discomfort. It is therefore clearly our responsibility and an obligation to do whatever we can to reduce stress and pain. In order to achieve this, we must keep abreast of the fields of research which are uncovering the information we rely upon to make these judgements. We must be constantly striving to improve our methods, equipment, abilities, to minimise any possible negative impact we have on the horse in the process of horse riding.

"Can you suggest one way that we, as equestrians, could make it better?"

BEVA has always placed the welfare of the horse at the forefront of what we do. We are conscious that owners, riders, and vets are particularly critical in safeguarding that welfare, and where evidence exists to demonstrate required changes in practice, BEVA prioritises dissemination of that information and education around how to apply the resulting knowledge. As a membership organisation for equine veterinary surgeons, BEVA prides itself in creating an interface for vets to communicate with the equestrian industry. If any message could be shared with horse riders, it would be to always remain curious about routines and habits, learn how to and monitor how comfortable and relaxed your horse is. We should be constantly questioning whether there is a better way of doing things, and where light can be shed on a better path to take, we should consider this as a partnership, and determine whether that path should be taken and always be prepared to alter course where evidence exists to suggest that.

"Could you give an example of how BEVA supports recognising pain in ridden horses?"

Pain is an emotion which produces behavioural changes in horses. We need to be attuned to these, as this is the only way they can communicate this emotion to us. Behavioural manifestations of pain can be as obvious as unloading a painful limb (lameness) to more subtle central signs of discomfort displayed as changes in facial expressions and normal behaviour, or avoidance activities.

"If you could reach out to horse riders with a slogan on a billboard, what would it say?"

"Understand your horse"

THE REGISTER OF ANIMAL MUSCULOSKELETAL PRACTITIONERS (RAMP)

Contribution from Jo Paul on behalf of RAMP
www.rampregister.org

As a voluntary regulator, the Register of Animal Musculoskeletal Practitioners (RAMP) maintains a register of highly skilled animal Physiotherapists, Chiropractors, and Osteopaths (Musculoskeletal Practitioners). RAMP does not take a view on whether the horse is better being ridden or not, RAMP is interested in horses getting the best possible care whatever their human/horse relationship.

The Animal Welfare Act 2006 puts responsibility on the owner to protect the horse from pain, suffering, injury and disease and most owners make best efforts to provide this. Sometimes that can be in the form of care from Allied Professionals such as Musculoskeletal Practitioners.

Finding a Musculoskeletal Practitioner you can trust to help your horse and do no harm can be a minefield. The titles of Physiotherapy, Chiropractic, and Osteopathy are not protected when it comes to treating animals as the law is separate and different from the human healthcare model. This makes it confusing for owners to identify fully qualified professionals.

Using the knowledge of experienced Practitioners, RAMP has set educational and professional standards heavily based on the human healthcare industry standards, as we believe animals deserve excellent care equivalent to that expected by humans. The register is freely available on the RAMP website www.rampregister.org for owners to check and see if the Practitioners they choose work to RAMP Gold Standards.

By using RAMP, you retain consumer choice by having access to the three professions safe in the knowledge that whoever you choose is regulated by an independent, impartial organisation who exists to protect the owner and their animals. Most importantly, you have peace of mind that you are truly employing only Practitioners using assessment led, evidence informed interventions who will communicate with other professionals in the team for best results to keep your horse comfortable whatever his job. RAMP uphold Gold Standards.

THE ASSOCIATION OF CHARTERED PHYSIOTHERAPISTS IN ANIMAL THERAPY (ACPAT)

Contribution from Sally Cinnamond on behalf of ACPAT
www.acpat.org

"In your opinion, how is horse riding good for a horse as well as a rider?"

Regular exercise (ridden and in-hand) helps to ensure the horse maintains strength and mobility, which is beneficial to horses of all ages and performance levels. This can help to prevent injury as well as facilitating optimal recovery post-injury. In addition, it is often beneficial to the management of many musculoskeletal and medical conditions.

"Can you suggest one way that we, as equestrians, could make it better?"

Ensure their horse is regularly assessed by an appropriately qualified physiotherapist to identify any areas of pain as well as any potential musculoskeletal restrictions or dysfunction. Physiotherapy involves a thorough clinical assessment to identify any musculoskeletal, neurological, cardiorespiratory and / or biomechanical dysfunction that could potentially limit optimal function and performance in your horse.

"Could you give an example of how ACPAT supports recognising pain in ridden horses?"

An ACPAT working group developed a Clinical Practice Guideline (CPG) based on review of current scientific and clinical information and accepted approaches to physiotherapy assessment. The CPG specifies that throughout the process of equine assessment, the physiotherapist should observe for facial and whole horse behaviours relating to signs of pain. There is strong evidence to relate both facial expressions and whole horse behaviours when ridden to the presence of musculoskeletal pain.

"If you could reach out to horse riders with a slogan on a billboard, what would it say?"

Regular physiotherapy assessment and treatment can help identify and / or prevent pain and musculoskeletal dysfunction in your horse. Ensure you book one regularly!

THE ASSOCIATION OF ANIMAL OSTEOPATHS (AAO)

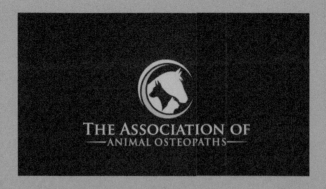

Contribution from Dustie Houchin on behalf of the AAO
www.associationofanimalosteopaths.com

"In your opinion, how is horse riding good for a horse as well as a rider?"

Early on, horses chose to accompany humans because they stood to gain from food, protection, and shelter. Today, however, it is the owner who chooses the horse, based upon their chosen need. Be that for sport, pleasure, or work. Each group has aspects that are positive for the horse and some that raise questions.

Racehorses, for example, experience high physical demands, but also have access to excellent facilities and accessories. A happy hacker on the other hand, may be loved by its owner, but needs to deal with the simplest type of tack and riding conditions. So, it is hard to say generically that one type of riding is better than the other, as the circumstances are so multi-faceted.

From a human perspective, riding is known to carry many benefits, be that exercise, a better state of mental health, companionship, competition and / or socialising with friends. We also know that in the world of professional equestrian sport, horses are associated with significant financial gain. So, one can see why owning a horse can be so attractive. However, most horse lovers also know that underneath the romantic façade of owning a horse, many contributing factors ensue and so, to conclude, I would say that it all comes down to a balance between objective welfare considerations versus the overall health of the horse.

"Can you suggest one way that we, as equestrians, could improve the horse-human interaction?"

Remember that horses don't think and react like humans, so understanding equine ethology and Applied Learning Theory will radically improve the way you work with your horse.

"Could you give an example of how the AAO supports recognising pain in ridden horses?"

Our Professional Practice and Educational Standards expect members to have the necessary clinical tools to evaluate an animal appropriately. In the case of pain, this might be the Horse Grimace Scale/Equine Pain Scale, which offers insight into the level of pain that a horse is experiencing. We also expect an animal osteopath to evaluate the horse's reactivity, sensitivity, breathing rate and ability to cope with its environment, as part of their initial consultation.

"If you could reach out to horse riders with a slogan on a billboard, what would it say?"

"Don't buy a Mini and expect a Ferrari"

THE MCTIMONEY CHIROPRACTIC ASSOCIATION (MCA)

Contribution from Daniel Piper and Katie Hopper on behalf of the MCA
www.mca-chiropractic.org

"In your opinion, how is horse riding good for a horse as well as a rider?"

For the rider horse riding can be a very positive form of exercise. It improves balance and coordination, core and leg strength, cardiovascular training, improved posture and can lead to better reflexes. For the horse, this can also be the case, but there are many elements in horse riding that affect how positive an outcome it is for the horse. Tack fit, correct farriery, and the ability and fitness of the rider are all factors that need to be considered to ensure the horse is being impacted positively when being ridden. When these variables have been considered, working the horse correctly will improve its fitness, balance and in turn its ability to carry the rider.

"Can you suggest one way that we, as equestrians, could improve the horse-human interaction?"

Being more aware of subtle signs that horses are not comfortable being ridden; horses are often tarred with having behavioural issues when really there is most likely a pain element to their behavioural changes.

Many times, when treating equine patients, the riders underestimate the importance of their own musculoskeletal health with it being put further down the list of all the horse's needs. This is akin to having a perfect car but an imperfect driver; the two need to be functioning optimally to perform at their best and to also protect themselves and each other from injury.

A normally functioning nervous system encourages optimum joint and muscle function and discourages injury. Prophylactically, this has the benefits of the animal and rider not being exposed to negative forces that can lead to injury and forced rest. Pain and behavioural changes are often much further down the list in signs of a malfunctioning musculoskeletal system. Periodic screening of the rider and horse can identify any nervous system issues that could lead to a breakdown in this protection.

"Could you give an example of how the MCA supports recognising pain in ridden horses?"

All MCA members are registered chiropractors, which means they can treat both horse and rider. MCA members are highly educated healthcare professionals with broad diagnostic skills and are competent to assess and treat appropriately using a range of chiropractic techniques. To assist owners and riders, the MCA provides guidance in the form of chiropractic leaflets explaining the more subtle signs that riders should look out for that may indicate that a horse may benefit from treatment. MCA members work closely with veterinarians, and other professionals when appropriate to make sure that a horse always receives the best possible evidence informed treatment. There is often a multidisciplinary and multidimensional approach to animal care.

MCA members work with both horse and rider and find early detection of issues through maintenance treatment will mean a better outcome for the horse than trying to treat an issue that has been low grade for a long time leading to compensation patterns.

"If you could reach out to horse riders with a slogan on a billboard, what would it say?"

'Horses are trying to communicate with us - we need to learn how to listen'

And an additional slogan for the rider:

"You are as important as your horse! Which underlines the fact as a rider you are an extension of the horse and not a separate entity, therefore ensuring your nervous system and skeletal functional symmetry is equal to that of the horse you ride."

THE SOCIETY OF MASTER SADDLERS

Contribution from the Society of Master Saddlers
www.mastersaddlers.co.uk

"In your opinion, how is horse riding good for the horse as well as the rider?"

Both horse and rider can benefit from horse riding. The relationship between horse and rider is one of trust, both parties can gain positively from this connection. From the horse's point of view, if it wasn't domesticated it would be happy to roam the plains and grasslands, however the modern horse we have created has changed considerably to its ancestors and as such we have a duty of care to look after it. A well-managed environment, good nutrition, exercise and stimulation of the domesticated horse is vital. Riding can improve the horse's mental well-being, physiology, proprioception and general fitness when managed and produced correctly.

"Can you suggest one way that we, as equestrians, could make it better?"

Most horse riders understand the management required to own horses and regularly seek the services of farriers, vets and other paraprofessionals. Often, riders undervalue the importance of their own needs, prioritising the horse.

All horse riders should see themselves as athletes and be the rider their horse would want them to be. Being aware of their own symmetry and fitness and taking steps to improve on this with the support of regular coaching, a human physiotherapist if required and riding related exercises, would make riding a better experience for the horse. Additionally, regular saddle checks and making small changes to saddle fit can make a big difference to comfort and stability for horse and rider.

"Could you give an example of how the SMS supports recognising pain in ridden horses?"

As part of our Qualified Saddle Fitter training, we train all our saddle fitters to fully assess the horse both statically and dynamically, in hand and ridden, paying particular attention to any musculature tension around the back and any gait asymmetry. We are often the first to notice subtle changes in muscle development from the templates taken at each appointment, as well as changes in how the horse moves under saddle. Identifying any changes in or loss of freedom of movement can be a precursor to other pain related issues. If we feel there is a problem outside of saddle or bridle fitting sphere, we can then refer the owners to their veterinarian or an appropriately qualified equine professional.

"If you could reach out to horse riders with a slogan on a billboard, what would it say?"

'FIT FOR WELFARE'

Regular saddle checks by Qualified Saddle Fitters at a minimum of 6 monthly intervals are recommended. Horses change shape through their development to maturity; seasonal changes can also affect saddle fit alongside changes in exercise, environment and nutrition. Bridle and bit fitting are also of equal importance to saddle fitting. It is imperative your horse is comfortable.

CHAPTER 7

Summary

*"I am still under the impression that there is
nothing alive quite so beautiful as a horse."*
John Galsworthy

CASE STUDY: **MICKEY**
By Hannah Knaebel-Seierstad

"His owner, in tears, said: 'I always thought it was my fault'."

Giselle and Mickey

Mickey came to Hannah aged five as a project, having become increasingly difficult for his previous owner to ride. His owner, Giselle, (an incredibly sweet, kind, older gal) had purchased him as a young horse, to be her last and final riding horse. She chose a Connemara, because she grew up in the UK riding Connemara 'ponies' and wanted her last horse to be like her first horse.

Even with a good start, Mickey was increasingly difficult for Giselle to ride by herself at home. He was happy on the trails, but any arena work would end up in a fight. There was lots of kicking and gnashing of teeth from Giselle and lots of balking and tail swishing from Mickey. He bounced around from trainer to trainer, getting a reputation for being fat, lazy and difficult. Trainers could sort him out, but within a week or two of returning home to his owner, Mickey would revert to bad behaviour. The only way Giselle could find happiness in being with him was by feeding him. She didn't feel safe riding him, so she spoiled him from the ground, until one day he pushed her down and injured her.

"He came to me mad and fat," remembered Hannah. "Spoiled, he would greet me with his mouth wide open and banging on the door. It took a couple of weeks of groundwork before I felt comfortable getting on him. After a week of walking under saddle, we started trot work. On a circle to the left, he felt ok. But going right, he started tripping, kicking out and slashing his tail, teeth bared and ears pinned. I got off and called the vet. Before the vet visit happened, an experienced colleague implied that 'It's probably just thin soles from being so fat…'. How can this attitude still exist, especially among professionals?"

A full lameness work up revealed bilateral hindlimb proximal suspensory desmopathy, and sesamoiditis in the left hindlimb. Mickey also had mild abnormalities in both stifles.

"The left hindlimb was nerve blocked, and he started limping on the right hindlimb under saddle, but he actually cantered two circles cleanly, which had been absolutely impossible before the block, and there was zero resistance in the trot. "His owner, in tears, said: 'I always thought it was my fault.'"

Following treatment, Mickey's work has been substantially downgraded.

"The system is broken"

Working as a coach, mentor and saddle-fitter, Hannah has first-hand experience of the devastating impact misunderstanding and misdiagnosis of pain and lameness in ridden horses can have. She shares her thoughts:

"Two things make me mad. First, there's the human cost, the shame that's put on vulnerable, naïve owners. That the horse 'needs more training rides' or that 'you're just not good enough'. No person should be made to feel bad about their skill. These poor owners started in horses because it brought them joy, and now they are reduced to shame because of ignorant, abusive trainers. The amount of time and money and tears spent is agonising. I desperately wanted Mickey's owner to understand that this wasn't her fault, that she did everything she could with the information she was given and that she was a better rider, because she wouldn't use coercive aids to force the horse to perform. People failed HER by not providing better information; she wasn't the failure.

"Then, there's the horse cost, which breaks my heart now I know more.

"As a saddle fitter, I saw a horse who slammed me into a wall when I began to palpate his back. The owner thought he just didn't trust strangers, but even as she took a bucket of treats for him to eat while I felt his back, he was stiff as a board, ears pinned, eyes bulging out of his head, with one hindlimb cocked. Her vet had told her he was just a bully and should be treated for ulcers and have his saddle checked. I asked the owner how he was under saddle. She replied, 'Oh, he's fine. Except I can't get him on the bit, and he swaps canter leads all the time, and he's really stiff through his top-line.'

"I forwarded her information on the RHpE. If I can show her that regardless of how he behaves on the ground, his behaviour under saddle can indicate pain, then we have a chance to help him, and in so doing, protect human life and limb as well. But why did her vet just leave a horse obviously in pain?

"I saw a Morgan gelding, whose owner had spent thousands of dollars on veterinary treatment. Her vet had indicated that the horse had a right stifle problem, although no nerve blocks had been performed and there were no radiological abnormalities. The owner wanted the saddle fit checked to be sure that it was not hindering the horse's rehabilitation after a long and tedious walking and groundwork programme. The saddle was an appropriate fit, but four steps into trot I asked her to halt because the horse was so lame behind.

"Her vet had treated the horse with ProStrideR (autologous protein solution) and PRP (platelet rich plasma), but neither had had a discernible effect. So, why are we putting needles into joints, why are we spending so much money, when we don't know exactly what the problem is? I encouraged the owner to pursue further diagnostics. She's frustrated because she feels the vets are just 'putting her off', because she's 'just an old lady with an old horse'. She feels they think it's not necessary to actually find a problem, that they can just treat in general and hope that the problem goes away. She asked me, 'Is it too much to ask that I can trot my horse for a lap or two?' No, I doubt that's too much to ask.

"There needs to be a new professional role created: a professional veterinary health care advocate, who works for the horse first, and also works as a go-between, to help facilitate the vet/owner communication. Someone who can help eliminate the major variables that people like to blame for behaviour, who can keep the vet moving through the horse until the problem is found. Too many times, vets 'peter out' before they get to the root of the problem.

"I'm sick and tired of broken horses, defeated owners, ignorant trainers, incomplete veterinary evaluations. I'm so frustrated with our broken system, of riding, of training, of diagnosis, of treatment. Horses pay the silent price, but there is great loss to their human owners – time, money, self-worth – because not enough people stop to ask the hard questions and dig for factual answers."

LET'S START WITH SOME QUESTIONS:

1. *Can you give three reasons why riding horses is good for the horse as well as for the human?*
2. *Explain why the RHpE is needed.*
3. *List eight of the 24 behaviours from the RHpE.*
4. *How can you use the RHpE with your own horse?*
5. *What options do you have if the RHpE score for your horse suggests that he is in pain?*

IN SUMMARY...

The Ridden Horse Pain Ethogram

Head above the vertical, ears back, an intense stare and mouth opening with separation of the teeth. The horse had a Ridden Horse Pain Ethogram score of 9/24.

The RHpE is a list of 24 behaviours, the majority of which are at least ten or more times likely to be seen in a horse with musculoskeletal pain than in a non-lame horse. Studies have shown that a horse which shows eight or more of the 24 behaviours of the RHpE is likely to have musculoskeletal pain. Don't be frightened or put off by the term ethogram; just think of it as a list of behaviours, a performance check list.

The horse as a happy athlete

A 'happy' event horse working comfortably

We all want to know that our horse is not in pain or discomfort. This book describes and explains the RHpE, how you can use it to help monitor your horse's quality of life, improve his performance, and its application relating to equestrianism's social licence to compete. Think of it as a performance behaviour check list. The supporting evidence has included case studies, contributions from relevant professionals and organisations, and a description of the science that got us to this point. Although it has been shown that high RHpE scores are associated with poorer performance in competitions from novice to top international levels, it has also been shown across the levels that the majority of horses have low RHpE scores, supporting the social licence for equestrian sports. However, the identification of those horses with high RHpE scores and appropriate investigation and management have the potential to improve both welfare (the 'happy' horse) and quality of performance. Moreover, the horse may be easier and more comfortable for the rider. We need to recognise better the appearance of pain-free 'happy' horses.

Lameness can be difficult to spot

It turns out we are not great at recognising lameness in horses. We all want to do the best for our horses, and to believe that they are happy and comfortable. To know that they are comfortable, we have to get better at recognising when they are uncomfortable. We can all see when a horse is obviously limping. But how about when it's just slightly unlevel, or when it's lame on more than one limb, or when it's just as lame on the right hindlimb as the left hindlimb, so the horse still moves symmetrically?

We know from the research that it can be difficult for veterinarians to agree which limb a horse is lame on, and the milder the lameness, the more difficult it is. We know it's easier to see forelimb lameness than hindlimb lameness. It's clear that a horse will use compensatory movements to adjust how weight is put through the lame limb(s) and how the horse pushes off with the lame limb(s), and we're starting to understand those compensations better, but they can make it hard to tell where the source of the problem is.

Less pain is linked to improved performance

All of this, and more, means that using behavioural assessments such as the RHpE to recognise lameness in the early stages could improve horse welfare. This could be useful, for example, when there's no lameness visible in hand, or when it's so low level that it's hard to see, or when the compensatory patterns of the horse's movement mask the lameness.

A 'happy' Grand Prix dressage horse working comfortably and likely to be high scoring

A study showed a link between higher RHpE scores and higher dressage penalties, a higher likelihood of elimination or retirement on the cross-country course, and a lower finish place at 5-star three-day event level. The most common RHpE score for horses competing at nine World Cup Grand Prix dressage competitions was low, at 3/24. There was a negative correlation between the RHpE score and judges' scores – so the higher the RHpE score, the lower the judges' score. The same relationship was observed at the British Grand Prix Championships, although the most frequent RHpE score was higher (6/24). At British Eventing 90, 100 and Novice one-day events horses placed first to third had significantly lower RHpE scores than horses with lower placings or non-finishers. So, there is clear fact-based evidence to say that comfort and quality of performance go hand in hand at all levels.

A 'happy' horse working comfortably competing at British Eventing 90 level

You can use the Ridden Horse Pain Ethogram with your own horse

You can use the RHpE with your horse. Ask someone to acquire video footage of you riding the horse for five to ten minutes, after your normal warm-up programme. Include walk, trot, and canter around the periphery of the arena (or an equivalent area on grass) on both reins, transitions within and between the paces, 10 m diameter circles in rising trot in a figure of eight, and any more advanced movements that you and your horse can perform as a partnership. Make sure that the video recordings include the horse moving in a straight line towards the camera and away from the camera from two different corners of the arena (or field). Watch the video as many times as necessary to work your way through the list of 24 behaviours, marking them as 'yes' or 'no'. A 'yes' scores 1, a 'no' scores 0. You may want to use a stopwatch for some of them, and / or a protractor to measure angles, to get a more accurate score. Watch the video footage full-screen on a lap top or personal computer; lameness or behavioural abnormalities can be missed on a small telephone screen.

Regular self-assessment is key

How about doing this exercise once a month with a friend, as part of monitoring your horse's well-being? You can record videos of your friend, and they can video you, and you can go through the videos together. Like any skill, using the RHpE will take practice, and it will get easier with time. Keep a record of your horse's score, and contact your veterinarian for further investigation, or another member of your horse's team if appropriate, if the horse scores eight or more out of 24 or if the scores are less than eight but are increasing over time. The earlier that a lameness is spotted, the easier it is to resolve it, in general.

The threshold is 8/24

Remember that a RHpE score of 8/24 is the threshold that suggests underlying musculoskeletal pain. So, if you're looking to get better results at competitions, or to be more confident that your horse is comfortable, and you want to proactively monitor his ridden behaviour, make use of the RHpE with your own horse on a regular basis. Rising scores, even if not reaching the threshold of 8/24, may still indicate the insidious onset of a problem. Some overtly lame horses have a RHpE score less than 8/24.

Other things to consider

There are other features which are not included in the RHpE that may be indicative of pain. Watch the horse's behaviour when tacked-up and mounted. A normal horse should stand quietly. Fidgeting, picking up forelimbs or hindlimbs, tossing the head, rubbing the nose against the wall, laying the ears back, turning the head to the girth region or attempting to bite are not normal during tacking up. Reluctance to stand at a mounting block, fidgeting or moving away are not normal behaviours during mounting. During ridden exercise teeth grinding or constant chewing on the bit are not normal. Consider the horse's respiratory (breathing) rate and recovery time after exercise and the amount the horse has sweated. A high respiratory rate, or delayed recovery time, or excessive sweating relative to the horse's fitness, the work intensity and duration, and the environmental conditions are likely indicators of an underlying problem.

Look out for more information

If you would like to learn more, please visit the Harmonious Horsemanship website at www.harmonioushorsemanship.co.uk. Here you can find up to date information and new links related to the content of this book. Within the book there is a list of the documented studies which describe development, validation and use of the RHpE, factors influencing RHpE scores, and the relationship between RHpE scores and competition performance, up to the date that the manuscript was submitted to the publishers. You can request copies of any of these studies from Dr Sue Dyson (sue.dyson@aol.com). However, research into the RHpE and its uses is ongoing, and you can find an up-to-date list on the website. There's an excellent online course on the RHpE available through Equitopia Center, which we highly recommend, and a freely available documentary online (available via https://www.24horsebehaviors.org/) which you can share with your friends and colleagues to raise awareness of this subject. Please keep in touch, and share with us your experiences and knowledge, so that together we can help to make the world a better place for horses and for their team.

TALKING POINTS

1. *Share your three key learning points from this book with your social media network.*
2. *How can you lead by example, to be part of the movement making the world a better place for horses?*
3. *Our message is that it is possible to recognise pain in ridden horses. What can you do to help us, the authors, to spread this message far and wide?*

SNIPPETS OF SCIENCE

"The Ridden Horse Pain Ethogram (RHpE) comprises 24 behaviours, the majority of which are at least 10 times more likely to be seen in lame horses compared with non-lame horses. The observation of ≥8/24 behaviours is likely to reflect the presence of musculoskeletal pain, although some lame horses score <8/24 behaviours. A marked reduction in RHpE scores after resolution of lameness using diagnostic anaesthesia proves a causal relationship between pain and RHpE scores..."

Dyson, S. The Ridden Horse Pain Ethogram. Equine Vet. Educ. 2022, 34(7): 372-380. https://doi.10.1111/eve.13468.

THE SADDLE RESEARCH TRUST

www.saddleresearchtrust.com

Contribution from Anne Bondi BHSI, BHSAPC, PGDip, DProf, on behalf of the Saddle Research Trust

"It's not you, it's me….

Many riders have problems in their relationship with their horse when riding. So often I hear riders saying things such as: "It's my own fault that my horse doesn't perform as well as it could; I'm wonky, so I make him go crooked; I don't sit straight so the saddle slips to one side; or I'm not a strong enough rider to make him go forwards".

I always say that a horse that is working comfortably can make an average rider look good, but that a horse that is uncomfortable can make even the most skilled rider look incompetent. A horse that is not compromised in any way should find the work easy and the rider should find him comfortable to sit on and easy to train, thus ensuring that the horse develops in a positive way, both mentally and physically.

The Saddle Research Trust has been actively involved with research studies investigating ridden horse behaviour over many years and campaigns for greater awareness of the use of the Ridden Horse Pain Ethogram (RHpE) or performance check list as a practical tool for all horse owners, riders, coaches, saddlery fitters, veterinarians, and other equine healthcare practitioners. There is now a great deal of evidence that in the majority of cases where there is a perceived "training problem", in fact the horse is working with an unrecognised pain related issue. With a lifetime's experience of owning, breeding, buying, training, riding, and competing horses, I have come to accept that the perfect horse does not exist, and we must therefore recognise, diagnose and manage appropriately, the problems that our horses face as they progress through their careers.

It is a fact that many horse owners believe that if a horse needs veterinary interventions such as, for example joint medication, then that horse should not compete at all. Many horse owners do not recognise when their horse is compromised, with the result that we see many horses out competing that are not comfortable in their work, many of whom never reach their potential or lose form and have short careers. I believe that if horses can be diagnosed accurately and treated appropriately, then we have a moral duty to do so if we wish to continue to subject them to the challenges of our equestrian sports. By doing so, we not only facilitate the horse to mature and develop as an athlete, we also help to protect our social licence to use horses for our pleasure if there are fewer unpleasant images to be seen in the competition world. This view may seem controversial, but I am also totally opposed to the widespread practice of medicating joints without first obtaining an accurate diagnosis.

It can, however, be extraordinarily difficult to accurately diagnose where the root of the problem lies – is it the horse, the rider, or the equipment that the horse is wearing that is creating or contributing to poor performance issues? Using the RHpE can be a powerful tool in recognising the signs that might otherwise be misinterpreted and intervening before a problem becomes irreparable. Common things happen commonly, and it has been extensively demonstrated that in an alarmingly high percentage of cases, it is lameness or a pain related issue in the horse that is the main cause.

So, let's stop always blaming the rider!

Authors' comment: This contribution has a personal flavour but has the approval and full support of the Trustees and the Executive Committee of the Saddle Research Trust.

CHAPTER 8

Frequently Asked Questions

1. To what extent are the behaviours of the Ridden Horse Pain Ethogram (RHpE) learned behaviour?

After resolution of either pain causing lameness or back pain using diagnostic anaesthesia ('nerve blocks'), there is almost immediate improvement in both gait and the majority of the 24 behaviours of the RHpE. This indicates that these are not learned behaviours, but are a direct response to pain.

However, effective hindlimb nerve blocks may induce a hindlimb toe drag, probably because of altered proprioceptive feedback from receptors in the frogs, so hindlimb toe drag may persist or even deteriorate in some horses.

We don't fully understand the mechanism which induces crooked tail carriage. It may be related to myofascial tension. We know that the frequency of occurrence of a crooked tail is more than eight times more in a lame horse compared with a non-lame horse. However, crooked tail carriage resolves completely after resolution of primary pain in only a small proportion of horses.

A horse which before resolution of pain had the front of the head in front of the vertical $\geq 30^0$ for ≥ 10s, may alter the head and neck position after resolution of pain so that the head is behind a vertical position.

We do not expect to see complete resolution of all behaviours, but we do expect to see a marked decrease in frequency of occurrence of the majority compared with before the use of nerve blocks. The persistence of many behaviours indicates that there must be additional sources of pain, for example an ill-fitting saddle.

2. Are there any of the behaviours of the RHpE which are less likely to change after resolution of pain?

See (1) above. It should be borne in mind that failure to substantially reduce the RHpE score after resolution of lameness means that there must be another source of pain. Consider oral pain, thoracolumbar pain (either primary, or secondary to an ill-fitting saddle or inappropriate distribution of the rider's weight), or lumbosacroiliac joint region pain or neck pain.

3. What is the influence of rider skill on RHpE scores?

A study was performed in which forty horses, that were in normal work and apparently working comfortably, were ridden by the normal rider and a single professional rider in a set dressage-type test (preliminary standard plus 10 m diameter circles in rising trot) of 8.5 minutes' duration, using the same tack and additional aids (spurs, whip). Fifty percent of horses were ridden first by the normal rider and then by the professional rider, and 50% were ridden first by the professional rider and then the normal rider. Rider skill (1-10), gait quality (1-10) and the presence or absence of lameness or abnormalities of canter were assessed independently. The RHpE was applied to video recordings of the tests.

Overall, the professional rider had a higher rider skill score than the normal rider. Gait quality was improved with the professional rider. There was a variable effect of rider skill on lameness – in some horses the lameness was less obvious when ridden by the more skilled rider, presumably because she balanced the horse better and rode forwards more. However, in other horses hindlimb lameness became apparent with the skilled rider because she was asking the horse to work harder, with increased hindlimb engagement and impulsion.

There was no significant difference in the number of behaviours shown between the normal rider and the professional rider, but some behaviours changed. For example, a horse changed from the front of the head in front of the vertical $\geq 30^0$ for $\geq 10s$, to the front of the head behind the vertical $\geq 10^0$ for $\geq 10s$. A horse that was not encouraged forwards by the normal rider appeared less willing with the professional rider because she was asking it to work harder.

So overall it was concluded that rider skill could not overcome the behavioural signs of discomfort, although a more skilled rider could improve gait quality and, in some horses, conceal lameness.

These are important factors to consider at pre-purchase examinations, when often the horse is ridden by a more skilled rider than the purchaser.

It has been our clinical observation that a rider who is extremely out of balance and unable to ride in synchrony with the horse's movement may exacerbate signs of lameness and pain-related behaviours.

We have also observed that uncomfortable horses are difficult to ride and may make a reasonably skilled rider appear less proficient than they would on a pain-free horse. If the horse is made more comfortable by removal of pain using nerve blocks, the horse becomes easier to ride and the rider looks much more effective and is better able to maintain their position.

There are some dressage horses that only show lameness or difficulties in performing movements when working in collection. Their behaviour under other conditions may be normal, but when asked to perform these more demanding movements, their behaviour deteriorates. A less-skilled rider may be unable to create adequate collection to cause discomfort and the demonstration of abnormal behaviour. A strong or very skilled rider may be able to 'make' a horse perform a movement which with a less skilled rider the horse may refuse to do (for example, it may stop and refuse to go forwards, 'planting'). However, the horse is highly likely to demonstrate other behaviours of the RHpE when ridden by the strong or very skilled rider.

4. What is the effect of rider position on RHpE scores?

It was demonstrated in a study of 148 horses in normal work and considered to be working comfortably by their riders, that there was an association between the RHpE scores and rider position. We noted higher scores for riders sitting on the caudal (back) third of the saddle compared with the middle of the saddle.

Rider position is affected by several factors – the shape, type, and size of the saddle (seat shape and size, flap size, position of knee and thigh blocks), the position of the stirrup bars, the morphology of the rider (height and relative lengths of the legs versus the trunk; 'bottom' size) and the ability of the rider to adopt and maintain a correct position.

The effect of a rider who sits crookedly has not been investigated, but asymmetrical weight distribution over a prolonged period is likely to result in adaptations of the horse's gait and ultimately pain, which may be associated with a progressive increase in RHpE scores.

5. What is the effect of rider size on RHpE scores?

In a study which involved six non-lame horses and four riders of similar ability but differing in height and weight, the riders were classified as Light, Moderate, Heavy or Very Heavy, based on the proportion of their bodyweight to the horses' body weights. Each horse was ridden in random order by the four riders, performing a dressage-type test of thirty minutes' duration, in walk, trot and canter. All the tests for the Very Heavy rider had to be abandoned early because of the development of transient lameness. All the tests for the Heavy rider were also abandoned early; five horses developed transient lameness and one horse had a RHpE score of 10 in canter, which was a criterion for abandonment. Retrospective analysis of video recordings of the tests showed that there were higher RHpE scores for the Heavy and Very Heavy riders compared with the Light and Moderate riders. There was a linear correlation between rider size and the RHpE score, but the RHpE scores did not exceed 6 at trot.

We believe that these effects of rider weight are at least in part related to rider weight distribution and forces under the saddle. The normal rider of Horse 2 weighed 92 kg, similar to the weight of the Heavy rider (91 kg). The normal rider was however considerably shorter than the Heavy rider and therefore sat in the middle of the saddle, whereas the Heavy rider sat on the caudal third of the saddle. The horse worked free from lameness with the normal rider, with a low RHpE score, whereas with the Heavy rider, the RHpE score was higher in association with the development of transient lameness.

See also (4).

6. Wouldn't you expect a young horse to show those behaviours included in the RHpE?

Assuming a horse is not in pain, we would not expect a horse to show ≥8 of the behaviours of the RHpE. A young horse may misunderstand a cue and react against it.

It may have an unsteady head carriage.

It may not easily go in a straight line when initially backed (introduced to ridden exercise).

It may open the mouth in response to a cue to perform a downwards transition, but we would not expect if to have its mouth open with separation of the teeth for ≥10s.

The front of the head may be in front of a vertical position, but not ≥30⁰

A young horse may be worried by the rider's weight and accelerate or buck. It may lay its ears back, but not persistently.

With repetitive correct training, a young horse should improve progressively as it better understands the rider's cues. Remember that each behaviour of the RHpE could be caused by a variety of factors; it is the total RHpE score which is important.

The gait quality of a young horse may change with the weight of a rider; a previously very free moving horse may move with more restricted gaits as it learns to adapt to the rider's weight, but assuming the horse is pain-free this should not be associated with a RHpE score of ≥ 8.

7. My trainer says that the horse won't go forwards because I don't have enough core strength. He suggests that I try long spurs. Is this true?

There are many reasons why a horse may not go forwards freely. It may be uncomfortable because of primary musculoskeletal pain or an ill-fitting saddle. The horse may lack hindlimb impulsion and engagement and impulsion because of pain in both hindlimbs or the thoracolumbosacral region (the back) without necessarily showing overt lameness.

The horse may misunderstand the rider's cues, or the rider may be applying cues ineffectively. Just because a more skilled rider can 'make' a horse go forwards more willingly, this does not exclude a pain-related problem. Application of the RHpE can help to determine the presence or absence of a pain-related problem.

We think that most pain-free horses are willing to go forwards, although they may perform better with a more skilled rider than a less skilled rider.

Treating the horse with a pain-relieving drug, such as phenylbutazone can help to determine if there is underlying pain, assuming that the horse is treated at a high enough dose for its body weight and for long enough (e.g., phenylbutazone 4.4 mg/kg twice daily for at least one week ± paracetamol 20 mg/kg BID and / or gabapentin 30 mg/kg [if neuropathic pain is suspected]). A positive response (improvement in performance) indicates the presence of musculoskeletal pain, but a negative response does not preclude the presence of musculoskeletal pain because phenylbutazone does not alleviate all forms of pain.

We generally advise keeping a diary of the horse's daily ridden performance for a week before treatment, during the week of treatment and for at least a week after stopping treatment. Improvement in performance during treatment or deterioration in performance after stopping treatment indicates the likely presence of pain.

8. How do you differentiate a training problem from pain-induced behaviour?

A horse may find it physically difficult to perform a movement or may misunderstand what is required of it. With correct training, we believe that any horse should be able to perform all dressage movements up to at least medium level. Depending on the athletic capability of a horse, it will do this with greater or lesser extravagance of movement. With progressive clear training, when a new movement is introduced, the horse should gradually improve the execution of the movement as it develops better musculoskeletal strength and coordination and neural pathways are consolidated.

A training problem that is unrelated to the presence of musculoskeletal pain should not be associated with a RHpE score of ≥8. If a horse can perform a movement easily on one rein but not the other rein, this usually reflects discomfort. It is important to be aware when teaching a new movement which requires a change in muscle use, that the horse may develop delayed onset muscular stiffness or soreness up to two days later. Delayed onset muscular soreness causes discomfort, but this should resolve within 24 to 48 hours. Be careful not to overtrain new movements. Be prepared to give the horse two to three easy days after the introduction of new movements that require recruitment of different muscle groups, or use of muscles in different ways (eccentric versus concentric contraction).

9. My horse repeatedly extends the upper muzzle when ridden, but never used to. Should I be concerned?

When the RHpE was originally developed, video footage of many lame and non-lame horses was compared and a list of 117 specific behaviours which might be associated with pain was created. Extension of the upper muzzle was one of the behaviours. The majority of the behaviours in the RHpE are at least ten times more likely to be seen in association with musculoskeletal pain compared with a non-lame horse. Those behaviours which were not included in the final RHpE may be associated with pain in some horses, and this includes extension of the upper muzzle. However, we would only be concerned if the horse showed 6, 7 or 8 or more of the behaviours in the RHpE.

Some other behaviours or observations which occur rarely in non-lame horses, that may be indicative of pain, but are not included in the RHpE are slack rein tension, leaning on the bit, yanking down on the reins, biting the chest, excessive chewing of the bit, teeth grinding, crossing the jaws (upper and lower teeth not aligned), deep wrinkle between the nostrils, sporadic and transient upwards tossing of the head, sweating excessively or abnormally high respiratory rate relative to the work intensity and duration, the horse's fitness and environmental conditions; grunting, adopting a 'saw-horse' posture after work.

10. Can gastric ulceration cause a RHpE score of ≥8?

We have not investigated the role of gastric ulcers alone and, in reality, there are few horses which have gastric ulcers that do not have concurrent lameness.

We have investigated many horses that present with a history of poor performance, have previously undergone gastroscopy, ulcers have been identified and treated with omeprazole ± sucralfate and despite resolution of the ulcers the horse's ridden performance and behaviour have not improved.

We suggest that gastric ulceration may arise because of the stress induced by working a horse with chronic musculoskeletal pain.

11. What influence does saddle fit have on RHpE scores?

We demonstrated in a study of 148 horses in normal work and considered to be working comfortably by their riders that there was an association between the RHpE scores and tight tree points. Horses with tight tree points had higher RHpE scores than horses with well-fitting saddles.

We have observed that abnormal movement of the saddle, a pommel or gullet that is too low, or a gullet that is too narrow, can all in some horses induce pain and behavioural abnormalities.

12. Why are so many horses lame?

Studies in Denmark, Switzerland, Sweden, and the United Kingdom have shown that > 50% of the sports and leisure horse populations are lame. In riding schools, the proportion of lame horses is higher. We suspect that the reasons are multifactorial starting with a failure to recognise low-grade lameness, so problems get worse and predispose to other problems, whereas if recognised at the time of onset, appropriate treatment may have resolved the problem long term. Many people learnt to ride at riding schools – so learnt on lame horses – so never developed a feel for what a normal horse should feel like and how a normal horse should respond to cues and behave. Ill-fitting saddles, riders being out of balance, or sitting crookedly, can all compromise the horse's movement and predispose to lameness. Current training methods are often poor. There is not enough focus on the horse going forwards, with good hindlimb impulsion and engagement, with good range of movement of the thoracolumbosacral region, and with the head in a vertical position or just in front of the vertical, NOT behind the vertical. Not enough attention is paid to the quality and maintenance of work surfaces and to cross-training on a variety of surfaces. Not enough attention is paid to rider position, left-right symmetry of weight distribution and to the ability to ride in synchrony with the horse. In addition, we are breeding for extravagant movement, rather than longevity.

13. Does the RHpE apply to leisure horses?

Absolutely yes. All the validatory work for the RHpE has involved both sports horses and leisure horses.

14. Does this mean that any lame horse should not be ridden?

In our opinion, the suitability of a lame horse for regular ridden exercise depends on several factors:

- What the horse is being asked to do and for how long.
- The degree of lameness.
- How willing the horse is, bearing in mind that some horses react to pain by trying to run away, which raises a question about rider safety.
- The degree of discomfort indicated by the RHpE score.
- The size of the rider and their ability, balance and fitness.
- What the diagnosis is of the cause of lameness, and if, based on the cause, there is a real risk of exacerbating the problem (for example, a tendon injury).
- Whether there are targeted treatments that can influence the cause of lameness, or non-specific treatments that can improve the level of discomfort.
- The horse's body condition score. The limbs of an overweight horse are being subjected to unnecessarily high loads.
- Whether there are changes in management that could help the horse.
- Whether there are treatments that can help to minimise pain associated with secondary problems, for example relief of muscle tension by physiotherapy interventions.
- The fitness of the horse and the regularity of ridden exercise.
- The nature of the footing; foot pain for example may be exacerbated on hard ground, ground with a camber, excessively stony ground or rutted ground.
- The nature of the terrain; steep hills may exacerbate hindlimb or forelimb pain. If the horse is reluctant to walk straight downhill or lacks power going uphill these are signs of discomfort.

There are many horses with mild lameness that does not deteriorate with work, which can work without undue discomfort and are willing to do so. Riders need to listen to their horses and make an informed decision about the level of pain based on the RHpE score. It should be borne in mind that hacking out or a cross-country ride are physically less demanding for a horse than repetitive circle work in an arena, and also provide enhanced mental stimulation. A lame horse may continue to jump satisfactorily provided that it is jumping well within its athletic capabilities and is not being continually asked for maximal musculoskeletal effort. Uncharacteristic stopping, running out or having rails down are often signs of discomfort.

15. Are there specific behaviours of the RHpE that horses with a specific problem show, for example, a horse with back pain?

The behaviours within the RHpE are non-specific and do not point to a particular source of pain. However, there are aspects of the whole clinical picture and history of the horse which may give clues as to the possible source of pain. For example, a horse with primary back pain may alter the gait in sitting trot compared with rising trot: in sitting trot the horse may have reduced range of motion of the thoracolumbar region (i.e., stiffen the back) and the head position may become more variable and there may be less consistency of rein tension. The regularity of the rhythm may change, with the horse either slowing or quickening the frequency of trot steps.

16. What is the influence on the behaviours of the RHpE of working in the proximity of other horses?

Horses which are racing against each other put their ears back. Some horses when working in a crowded arena get intimidated by the close proximity of other horses and may show some abnormal behaviours, but we would not expect this to dramatically change RHpE scores. Some horses may appear more willing to go forwards freely in the company of other horses than when alone.

17. Does the RHpE work in western performance horses?

The RHpE has not been systematically tested in western performance horses, but, based on a pilot study, the same principles should apply. Obviously, head and neck position will in part be dictated by what western performance discipline a horse is involved in. However the not uncommon practice of blocking tails may prohibit application of the behaviours repeated tail swishing and crooked tail.

18. How do normal horses behave when they jump? Are there any specific signs of pain in jumping horses?

The RHpE has not yet been systematically tested during jumping, but most normal horses have their ears forwards over a fence and on landing. The ears may go back on the approach, especially if the rider is restraining the horse.

The head may be elevated on the approach to a fence, with the front of the head ≥30⁰ in front of a vertical position. Depending on how the horse has been trained, it may tilt the head on turns.

A normal horse should not repeatedly change legs behind in canter. It should push off squarely with both hindlimbs and jump straight across the fence without deviating to the left or right. It should not stop or run out unless poorly trained or badly presented to a fence. The horse should land with the correct leading forelimb. Bucking on landing is not normal, and contrary to popular belief is usually not a sign of 'joie de vivre', but pain. Lack of power, putting in short steps to take off close to a fence, or having difficulty in making distances in combination fences, usually reflect pain. If a horse was previously careful and seldom had rails down but has started having fences down more often this usually reflects discomfort. If a horse has rails down when close to a fence but not when taking off further away from the fence this often reflects hindlimb or pelvic discomfort. Rushing or unwillingness to jump drop fences or fences into water may all relate to discomfort. Ears back over a fence and/or on landing is not normal.

19. Isn't the head being behind a vertical position induced by the rider?

The position of the horse's head and neck is in part dictated by the rider, and a skilled rider should be able to adjust the head and neck position. If a skilled rider cannot alter the position of the horse's head, this is not normal, particularly if there is reduced or no rein tension. In our experience, head behind vertical ≥10⁰ with reduced rein tension is commonly a reflection of discomfort; when horses perform more biomechanically difficult movements (for example 10 m diameter circles in rising trot, piaffe), the head often goes further behind the vertical with further reduction in rein tension. If pain is removed by nerve blocks, the horse usually raises the head to a vertical position with increased rein tension.

20. Why is teeth grinding not included in the RHpE?

The original development of the RHpE was based on the assessment of video recordings of non-lame and lame horses. Although audio was present and the video recordings were zoomed to keep the horses filling the screen, audio recording from the far end of arenas was not reliable. Therefore, recording teeth grinding was not reliable. Nonetheless, we believe that teeth grinding is not normal and is generally a reflection of discomfort.

21. Who can apply the RHpE?

Anyone can apply the RHpE, but like any clinical skill it requires education and training, practice, and development of observational skills. It is important to be fully aware of the definitions, noting that many include 'repeatedly' and that others specify a minimum time of the behaviour, which needs to be timed. It is advisable to use a checklist.

22. If I think that my horse may have pain based on the RHpE, what should I do next? My vet says that the horse is not lame.

Firstly, we have to acknowledge that there are general purpose equine veterinarians and those who have developed more specialist skills and undergone some form of post graduate further education. Conventionally, most vets have been taught to evaluate horses moving in hand and on the lunge. There has been no tradition of assessment of canter, nor evaluation of horses during ridden work. It is now recognised that there are many horses which do not show lameness in hand but do exhibit lameness when ridden. It is also recognised that a horse may be able to trot comfortably but struggle in canter because of musculoskeletal pain.

Secondly, it is necessary to be aware that a human athlete with a problem is much more likely to consult a sports medicine specialist rather than their local general practitioner. Any owner is entitled to a second opinion and your regular vet cannot refuse this; in fact, we suggest that they should encourage this. The horse needs to be evaluated by a veterinarian who has the prerequisite skills to evaluate the horse not only in hand and on the lunge, but also ridden, and who understands how horses can adapt to musculoskeletal pain in many ways, including compromising performance. The veterinarian must be prepared to do nerve blocks to determine the sources of pain, which includes reassessing the horse ridden. Ideally, the veterinarian should also have an understanding about the importance of saddle fit for horse and rider, and the large influence an ill-fitting saddle can have on performance. Changing to a better fitting saddle may be an important part of the investigation.

23. With my last horse the vet recommended a bone scan, found some hot spots, and treated these, but the horse did not get better. Does this mean the horse was not in pain?

No, it does not mean that your horse was not in pain. A bone scan tells us about bone activity, but not about pain. A region of increased radiopharmaceutical uptake (a 'hot spot') does not necessarily equate with pain. There can be incidental hot spots and also false negative results, especially for injuries involving either joints or soft tissue structures. In our experience, a bone scan is frequently not a useful technique to use in the investigation of a sports horse performing poorly and this was confirmed by a retrospective study comparing 'blind' reading of scintigraphic images and the results of investigation using nerve blocks, radiography, ultrasonography ± magnetic resonance imaging (MRI). There was a high proportion of inaccurate results. It is much more important to perform a very thorough clinical assessment, which must include ridden exercise, and then use nerve blocks to determine the sources of pain. When the sources of pain have been identified, then radiography (x-rays) and ultrasonography (with or without computed tomography, commonly known as CT, or MRI) should be used to establish the cause(s) of pain. Only then can a logical treatment and management plan be developed.

24. My horse has always been grumpy, that's just how she is, she's 'mare-ish'. How do you differentiate a 'hormonal horse' from one that has underlying pain?

We genuinely do not believe that there are pain-free grumpy horses, so it is likely that the horse does have chronic discomfort. Horses do have variable temperaments, and the behaviour of a mare can be affected by hormonal cycles, however these behaviours usually include clitoral winking, frequent urination, squatting, elevation of the tail and increased tolerance. Suppression of the oestrus cycle using Regumate[R] (altrenogest, a synthetic progestin) allows separation of behaviours which may be associated with being a mare in season compared with behaviours associated with pain. There are many signs attributed by owners to moodiness in mares including aggression, anxiety or nervousness, sensitivity around the flanks or girth region, being difficult to handle, ears back, resistant, repeated tail swishing, excessive urination, kicking and generalised decrease in performance. However, these are not generally the signs demonstrated by a mare in season.

25. My horse jumps fine, so he cannot be in pain, but he dislikes flat work.

We are afraid that this is a myth. Many horses enjoy jumping. Jumping also results in the release of adrenaline and endorphins, which can result in pain suppression. So, there are many horses that struggle with flat work because of chronic discomfort but jump satisfactorily, assuming that they are jumping well within their athletic abilities. A horse which is said 'not to like' flat work, or has to be worked in for a long period because 'otherwise he is too tense', usually has underlying pain-related problems. Working continually with turns and circles is more biomechanically demanding than working in straight lines, so flat work may exacerbate pain. In addition, the horse's attitude must also be considered – repetitive flat work is boring, compared with the excitement of jumping. Riders often ride more positively when jumping compared with flat work and encourage the horse forwards more, which may also apparently improve performance.

Jumping may only become compromised when pain is exacerbated, for example a horse with front foot pain being asked to jump drop fences. Alternatively, if the horse is being asked to jump repetitively to the maximum of its athletic capabilities, its performance may reduce, especially if the take-off spots are not ideal.

For further information about 'equestrian myths' go to:

https://www.worldhorsewelfare.org/advice/health/ridden-issues-troubleshooting-unwanted-behaviours

26. My horse struggles to maintain canter and has been like this since I bought her. She 'passed' a PPE (a pre-purchase examination, commonly known as a vetting) and my vet says she's not lame, so surely that means she cannot be in pain?

We believe that a pain-free horse should be able to establish and maintain canter either in straight lines or within the confines of an arena on the left and right reins with equal ease. Some horses need to learn how to canter with the weight of a rider and teaching them this when cantering out hacking or in a large field, with the rider in a two-point position is often best. There are horses which do not show signs of discomfort or overt lameness in trot in hand, on the lunge or ridden, but which struggle to maintain canter. This is usually the result of pain.

It must be borne in mind that at a pre-purchase examination, although ridden exercise is part of the examination in the United Kingdom, it is not in many other countries. Moreover, many veterinarians view the ridden phase of the examination as a time to assess the cardiovascular and respiratory responses to fast exercise. I (Sue Dyson) advocate that the ridden phase should always include flat work so that the horse is observed in walk, trot and canter, including transitions between all paces. I believe that this is crucial because there are many horses which appear sound in hand but show lameness or other gait abnormalities when ridden. So, the likelihood is that this horse is experiencing pain, unless she is a young horse which has not developed sufficient musculoskeletal strength and coordination to maintain canter.

27. Is there a difference between head shaking and head tossing?

True head shaking is a behaviour which may be seen in a stable, turned out, or on the lunge or ridden, and is characterised by spontaneous displays of uncontrollable, sometimes violent episodes of repetitive vertical, horizontal, or rotary movements of the head and neck. Head shaking is believed to be related to nerve pain mediated via one of the facial nerves, the trigeminal nerve.

Excessive sneezing or snorting, acting like an insect was flying up the nostril, rubbing and / or striking at the nose with the forelimbs are often to be seen in horses with trigeminal-mediated head shaking, which may be seasonal, occurring only in the summer months in some horses.

Head tossing is a vertical up and down movement of the head during ridden exercise, which is usually a non-specific sign of musculoskeletal pain and is one of the behaviours of the RHpE. Head-tossing behaviour is abolished when the primary source(s) of pain causing abnormalities of gait are removed by nerve blocks.

28. Can oral pain influence behaviour?

Pain coming from the mouth can unquestionably cause pain that influences behaviour. Sources of pain include sharp teeth edges rubbing the inside of the cheek (the buccal mucosa) resulting in erosions or ulcers, an infected tooth root, a cut at the commissure of the lips and a bit which is of inappropriate shape and size for the shape and size of the mouth and the tongue. A bit which has sharp edges or the rings of a loose ring snaffle bit also have the potential to induce pain. The use of overly strong rein cues (aids) may also cause pain. Occasionally a large unerupted vestigial cheek (premolar) tooth (wolf tooth) may cause discomfort.

29. What is the potential effect of an over-tight noseband?

The effect of an over-tight noseband depends in part on the noseband type (e.g., cavesson, crank cavesson, flash, crank flash, Micklem, grackle, drop) and where on the face that it is positioned, the width of the noseband, the stiffness of the leather and the distribution of any padding, the presence or absence of side rings, the position of buckles and the stability of the noseband. These factors will influence the magnitude and the distribution of pressures applied by the noseband.

The distribution of pressure is also influenced by the shape of the horse's head. The distance between the lower end of the facial crest and the commissures of the mouth, the distance between the commissures of the mouth and the end of the chin and the relative distances between the upper (the front of the face to the level of the mouth) and lower (from the mouth to the back of the lower jaw) vary considerably among horses. The profile of the lower aspect of the jaw varies according to age, with prominences in young horses because of the mandibular teeth.

There is the potential to compress superficial facial nerves, to restrict movement of fascia, to put undue pressure on the ventral part of the mandible (the lowest aspect of the jaw bone) and to compress the cheek (the buccal mucosa) against the premolar and molar (cheek) teeth. A noseband could theoretically restrict mouth opening and limit movements of the upper and lower jaws.

Noseband fit should also consider the headpiece of the noseband which has the potential to cause pressure points at the back of the ears and which is in close proximity to the temporomandibular joint and attachments of muscles that influence movement of the head and neck and forelimb protraction. An ill-fitting headpiece part of the noseband has the potential to influence head and neck flexion and forelimb protraction.

These observations highlight the need to individualise noseband fit and other aspects of the bridle (headpiece, browband and bit), in combination with routine and tailored dental care. It should be borne in mind that the use of a noseband has the potential to enhance overall stability of the bridle, which can be a good thing.

30. Why do horses open their mouths?

There are many reasons why horses open their mouths during ridden exercise. Mouth opening may be a non-specific response to musculoskeletal discomfort. Alternatively, it may reflect oral discomfort secondary to the buccal mucosa being pressed against the sharp edges of the teeth by a tight noseband, or other oral lesions, excessive rein tension, movements of the rider's hands, or the type and size of the bit(s) relative to the size and shape of the horse's oral cavity and tongue. We have observed that if horses are lunged wearing their own bridle and then ridden, the frequency of mouth opening is substantially higher during ridden exercise.

The frequency of occurrence of mouth opening with separation of the teeth for ≥10s was higher in horses competing at five-star three-day events compared with British Eventing 90, 100 and Novice one-day events. An even higher occurrence of mouth opening was observed in Grand Prix dressage horses, especially those competing at sub-elite level. Whether this reflects the use of double bridles, the prevalence of musculoskeletal pain, or the cues from the riders, remains to be determined.

31. Why does my horse yawn after I remove the bridle?

Yawning is considered to be a stereotypical behaviour and can be observed as a result of stress (for example during tacking-up, in anticipation of pain during ridden exercise either because of musculoskeletal pain or an ill-fitting saddle) or as a rebound response after a stressful situation (pain during ridden exercise because of musculoskeletal pain or an ill-fitting saddle). However, yawning when seen in isolation, unrelated to tacking-up or after ridden exercise, does not necessarily indicate that anything is wrong. Horses often yawn during physiotherapy treatment. Along with the yawning, it's common for the horse to drop the head and half close the eyelids, in apparent relaxation. This behaviour appears to be linked to a release of muscle tension, and therefore perhaps to an improvement in the level of comfort, so a rebound response. As with people, the reasons behind yawning are not well understood, and are likely to be related to a variety of different causes.

32. Why does my horse try to bite (girth aversion behaviour) when tacked-up?

Biting is an aggressive behaviour which may be stress-induced. We have shown that there is an association between abnormal behaviours during tacking-up, and the presence of primary musculoskeletal pain during ridden exercise or an ill-fitting saddle, especially tight tree points of the saddle. A small proportion of horses with equine gastric ulcer syndrome may show this behaviour (also see 10).

We have also observed biting in association with rugging which we suspect is probably related to chronic musculoskeletal pain, although this is yet to be proven.

33. My horse now refuses to stand at the mounting block when I get on. Why might this be?

Refusing to stand while mounted could reflect inadequate training and is potentially correctable. However, it also may be a behaviour which reflects anticipation of pain during ridden exercise, because of primary musculoskeletal pain or an ill-fitting saddle.

34. My horse tries to bite his chest at the end of ridden exercise. Why does this happen?

I (Sue Dyson) have observed this behaviour (attempting to bite the chest) in horses which were competing at British Eventing 90, 100 or Novice levels either during free walk on a long rein, or at the end of dressage tests in the final halt ± leaving the arena at walk. It was only observed in horses with high RHpE scores, and I assume that it is a stress-induced stereotypical behaviour.

35. My horse's behaviour has become unpredictable when ridden. On some days, she seems calm and cooperative, but on other days she is tense and may spook or suddenly try to accelerate. Is this because of pain?

Unpredictable behaviour in our experience is usually pain-induced. Pain may vary in degree from day to day. Spookiness and changes in speed are two behaviours of the RHpE. Tension is not something that is easy to define specifically by observation, but typically is manifest as lack of relaxation, over-reactivity to leg cues, reduced response to rein cues – lack of 'ride-ability'. We have observed this many times in horses with musculoskeletal pain, or an ill-fitting saddle, and these behaviours usually disappear when the source of pain is removed.

36. My horse 'hangs' on the left rein, but I'm aware that my left side is stronger than my right. I am left-handed. Should I be concerned?

A correctly trained, pain-free horse should take an even rein contact (so rein tension is symmetrical). Some horses which have not been properly trained do not bend correctly around corners and take a stronger contact in one rein than the other. There is usually a reduction of or lack of rein tension in the other rein.

So, a horse may hang on the left rein, especially on the left rein, and 'fall in' on the left rein, but on the right rein tend to bend the neck excessively to the right. I (Sue Dyson) would ride 20 m diameter circles in rising trot. On the left rein on the circle, I would ask the horse to bend the head and neck to the right (to the outside) to try to get the horse to 'take' the right rein cue, while applying a firm inside leg cue. After maintaining this flexion to the outside for several strides, I would then release the right rein cue. I would repeat this several times and on release of the right rein cue, expect the horse to take a better contact with the right rein, so that the contact on the left and right sides became more even. Ultimately, I would expect to be able to give and retake the left rein, with the horse maintaining the contact via the right rein. I would expect that with this straightening the quality of the trot steps would progressively improve. By switching work between the left and right reins, I would hope to be able to maintain this evenness in rein tension.

However, uneven rein tension may be an adaptation to lameness, especially hindlimb lameness, and the use of 'counter-flexion' may fail. If lameness is abolished by nerve blocks, then the rein tension immediately becomes more symmetrical. This indicates that asymmetrical rein tension does in some horses reflect lameness.

37. I am not sure if my event horse is right, so I used the RHpE several times, and the score is only of 7/24. Could he still have pain?

All our studies have shown that a RHpE score ≥8 is an indicator of the presence of musculoskeletal pain, but some lame horses have a RHpE score of <8.

So yes, your horse could have pain.

We have statistically compared thresholds of 6,7,8 and 9 and the threshold of 8 gives the most accurate results (highest combined specificity and sensitivity). However, in studies looking at the performance of lower level (BE 90, 100 and Novice) and elite (five-star three-day event) event horses and Grand Prix dressage horses at all levels there is a correlation between RHpE scores and performance. So overall, the higher the RHpE score is (even if <8), the worse the horse is likely to perform. Five-star three-day event horses with a RHpE score ≥7 were more than twice as likely to be eliminated or retire cross-country, than horses with a RHpE score <7, and if they completed the event had lower finish places.

38. My horse is a 6-year-old chestnut mare. She is very tense and anxious when ridden. I've been told that this is normal for chestnut mares. Is this true?

There is no scientific evidence to support the idea that colour or sex influence ridden horse behaviour, unless behaviour is hormonally driven and related to the oestrus cycle. Abnormal tension often reflects underlying musculoskeletal pain and is usually associated with other behaviours included in the RHpE.

39. I have become very apprehensive about riding my horse. When I bought her, she seemed quiet and reliable and she has a wonderful temperament which does not seem to have changed. She has become spooky and will suddenly

stop and spin or accelerate rapidly when ridden but is really easy to handle in a stable or a field. My trainer tells me that I should ride her more positively, but my instinct tells me that there is something wrong. What should I do?

A change in ridden horse behaviour usually occurs because of underlying musculoskeletal pain, so we think that you need alternative professional advice to determine the underlying cause. Nonetheless it is true that a horse's behaviour can also be influenced by the confidence and skill of the rider, and a vicious circle can occur if you continue to ride the horse. We therefore suggest that the horse undergoes investigation by a veterinarian and assuming that the underlying problem is identified and treated successfully, when first resuming ridden work get the help of a more confident rider. Hopefully you will see a return to the horse which you knew before, which should help to restore your confidence.

40. My horse, an 11-year-old gelding that I use for Riding Club activities, has recently become unwilling to go down to the arena. He has always been a lazy horse ever since I bought him and is more difficult to maintain in left lead canter than in canter to the right. This has not changed despite regular lessons with a trainer. Should I be concerned?

A normal horse that has been correctly trained should not be lazy and should be able to canter easily on both the left and right reins. The unwillingness to walk down to the arena is probably a reflection of anticipation of pain. It seems likely that your horse has always had pain-related performance problems which may be deteriorating. This is likely to be reflected by a RHpE score of eight or more. Further investigation is merited.

41. My horse has started to fidget and sometimes picks up a hindlimb when I place the saddle on her back. She seems less willing than before when I ride her, but I cannot detect any lameness. I asked my saddle-fitter to check the saddle and she advised me that the saddle was the likely cause. We tried several saddles, none of which seemed to fit the horse perfectly or alter her ridden behaviour, so my saddle-fitter advised that I had a custom-made saddle. I agreed, but I am really disappointed that the horse's behaviour when tacked up and ridden has not changed, despite me spending a lot

of money. Does this mean that the saddle was not the cause of the horse's change in behaviour?

In our experience a so-called custom-made saddle does not necessarily fit perfectly the horse for which it was designed. We would therefore certainly recommend that the saddle-fit is checked by an independent expert. We would expect that if the saddle was the primary problem the horse's ridden behaviour should immediately improve substantially when ridden in a saddle which correctly fits both the horse and the rider. However, it may take several weeks being ridden in a correctly-fitted saddle before the tacking-up behaviour improves. It is also possible that there may be an additional source of musculoskeletal pain which requires investigation.

42. My horse that competes at BE 100 level used to show jump in a regular rhythm, but recently, in the last two months, she has started to 'suck-back' on the approach to a fence and then charges at each fence. My trainer says that I am 'over riding' the horse. I was very confident competing at BE 90 and we regularly jumped clear rounds. We moved up to BE 100 level about six months ago and initially our show jumping performances were fine.

Such a change in show jumping performance could possibly relate to your riding but it is, in our opinion and experience, more likely that this reflects underlying musculoskeletal pain and merits investigation. Bilateral front foot pain or bilateral hindlimb lameness are common causes of a change in jumping performance.

43. My 7-year-old Warmblood gelding works at medium dressage level. He takes time to 'warm up' but seems to 'work out of it'. My trainer tells me that this is normal for horses. In my heart the horse does not feel 100%. He usually scores about 63% in tests and a consistent comment is that the canter should have more energy. What should I do?

An older horse with known musculoskeletal problems may start working a little stiffly and progressively improve with time during a work session. A pain-free horse of 7 years of age should work freely from the outset. Lack of hindlimb impulsion and engagement in canter could reflect a training problem, but it is more likely in this situation to reflect a low-grade bilateral hindlimb lameness which needs investigation sooner rather than later before other secondary problems develop.

44. I bought my 6-year-old Warmblood dressage horse six months ago. He seemed weak at first and heavy in the hand. My trainer advised me that I needed to develop more core strength, so I have been working with a personal trainer, but the horse's performance has not changed although I feel much fitter and more toned. The horse does flat work three times a week, and hacks three times a week up and down rolling hills. My trainer has now advised that I should switch to a double bridle. What should I do?

A 6-year-old pain-fee horse which is worked regularly and is adequately fit should be developing self-carriage and strength and should not lean on the bit. Heaviness in the hand usually means that the horse is working on the forehand and lacks hindlimb impulsion and engagement. This may be pain-induced and should be investigated.

45. My 12-year-old advanced event horse is performing well but struggles with flying changes, especially from left to right, and the more I practice the worse the changes seem to get and the tenser he becomes. My trainer advised going back to basics and practising walk, canter right, walk, canter left transitions and trying flying changes over poles on the ground. I've tried this with no improvement. Is there anything else that I can do?

The most common reasons for difficulties with flying changes are hindlimb lameness or lumbosacroiliac joint region pain. Identification of the underlying source of pain and appropriate management should improve the flying changes. You may also be surprised by how much the overall quality of the horse's work and demeanour improve.

Acknowledgements

CONTRIBUTORS TO THE BOOK

Guest contributors:

Dr Rosie Jones McVey, Dr Lynda Birke, Dr Jo Hockenhull, Dr Jessica Mullard, Dr Tamzin Furtado, Dr Jessica Kidd, Mark Aikens, Ellie Tomlinson, Sonya Nightingale, Dr Vav Simon, Eleanor Andrews, Grant Chanter, Claire Macleod, Kelly Marks, Boo Riley, Mary Wanless.

Horse owners:

Alice Clurow, Kathy, Hannah Knaebel-Seierstad, Hayley Redding, Rachel (name changed for anonymity), Claire Martin, Thea Roberts, Giselle, Heidi Hunter-Cope, Anne Bondi, Joanne H.

Contributing organisations / associations / governing bodies:

Human Behaviour Change for Animals
British Equine Veterinary Association
Register of Animal Musculoskeletal Practitioners
Association of Chartered Physiotherapists in Animal Therapy
Association of Animal Osteopaths
McTimoney Chiropractic Association
Society of Master Saddlers
Saddle Research Trust

EDITORIAL ASSISTANCE

Polly Bryan

IMAGE CREDITS

Peter Dove: page 149
Sue Dyson – all the rest
Sarah H: page 179
JT Photography: page 123
Tracy Kidd: page 156
Martha Lily Photography: Front matter, pages 106, 126, 152, 153
Ele Milwright: page 21
Simon Palmer: pages xvi, 200
Emma Parkinson Equine and Pet Photography: pages 1, 3
Aubrey Roth: page 194
Nickolett Uhler: page 26
Matthew Webb: page 145

PRINCIPLE COLLABORATORS IN THE RHpE STUDIES

Dr Jeannine Berger, Dr Anne Bondi, Dr Andrea Ellis, Helene Dragelund Garcia, Dr Casper Lindegaard, Claire Martin, Dr Jessica Mullard, Dr Danica Pollard, Dr Laura Quiney, Dr Jenny Routh, Dr Katy Thomson, Dr Jan Van Dijk

OTHER COLLABORATORS IN THE RHpE STUDIES

Use of the RHpE by non-trained assessors

Julie Breingan, Cheryl Chan, Siobhan Gilligan, Melissa Lockwood, Islay MacLaren, Laura Quiney, Emma Reeder, Heather Stephenson, Karen Sweet and Katy Thomson

Rider skill study

Daniel Cook, Robin Gill and Jane Hart for facilitating arrangements at Writtle University College. Lizzie Cairns for facilitating arrangements at the private livery yard. Victoria Mensley, who called the tests; Georgie Welge, Society of Master Saddlers Qualified Saddle Fitter; Rhian Williams, Veterinary Physiotherapist; Karen Sweet, professional rider; and the horse owners.

Ability of veterinarians to apply the RHpE study

Jo Spear, Association of Chartered Physiotherapists in Animal Therapy member; Liz Suddaby, Society of Master Saddlers Qualified saddle fitter; the Society of Master Saddlers; James Bowdler, Mike Daly, Lucy Grieve, Vicky Hall, Roxane Kirton, Lucy Meehan, James Risk, Katy Thomson, Helen Whitbread, Simon Woods, the veterinary assessors; Annie Pollock, Julie Breingan, Melissa Lockwood, Karen Sweet, Sam White and Mollie Stephens, who provided technical help; and the horse owners.

FUNDING AND EDUCATION

Equitopia

Source of the training course 'How to recognise the 24 behaviours indicating pain in the ridden horse'

Padma Videos

Kathryn Lauritzen, co-producer of the documentary 'The 24 behaviors of the ridden horse in pain: Shifting the paradigm of how we see lameness'

Saddle Research Trust

Financial support for the preliminary studies on the development of the RHpE and promotor of the use of the RHpE through education

World Horse Welfare

Financial support for the preliminary and validation studies for the RHpE and promotor of the use of the RHpE through education. Co-production and circulation of 'Myth busters'.

RIDERS

Karen Sweet, Rachel Cawley, Rachel Grundon, Siobhan Gilligan, Jessica Cooke, Claire Martin

PUBLICATIONS RELATED TO THE RIDDEN HORSE PAIN ETHOGRAM AND OTHER SOURCES OF INFORMATION

For more information

The details on this page are correct at the time of going to press (2023), but this is a rapidly emerging field of interest, and so the amount of information available is expected to grow.

Website

www.harmonioushorsemanship.co.uk

Documentary: *The 24 behaviors of the ridden horse in pain: Shifting the paradigm of how we see lameness*

www.24horsebehaviors.org

Online course: *The 24 behaviors of the ridden horse in pain*

www.equitopiacenter.com

Myth busters: *World Horse Welfare*

www.worldhorsewelfare.org/advice/health/ridden-issues-troubleshooting-unwanted-behaviours

Contact details

Sue Dyson: sue.dyson@aol.com
Sue Palmer: www.thehorsephysio.co.uk

Publications related to the RHpE

Those marked with an asterisk(*) are Open Access and are available via the URL. Any paper can be shared with individuals, please contact Sue Dyson by e-mail at sue.dyson@aol.com.

Berger, J., Bondi, A., Dyson, S., Ellis, A., Lindegaard, C., Martin, C Mullard, J., Pollard, D., Quiney, L., Routh, J., Thomson, K. (2022) Letter to the Editor: Commentary on Ladewig et al. : The value, uses and limitation of the Ridden Horse Pain Ethogram. *J. Vet . Behav.: Clin. Appl. Res.* 57, 31-34.

*Dragelund Garcia, H., Lindegaard, C., Dyson, S. (2023) Application of a Ridden Horse Pain Ethogram in Icelandic Horses: a Pilot Study. *Equine Vet. Educ.* doi:10.1111/eve.13803

Dyson, S. (2019) Application of a ridden horse ethogram to horses competing at a 4-star three-day-event: comparison with cross-country performance. *Equine Vet. J.* 51 (Suppl. 53), 11.

Dyson, S. (2020) Unexplained forelimb lameness possibly associated with radiculopathy. *Equine Vet. Educ.* 32(S10), 92-103.

Dyson, S., Berger, J., Ellis, A., Mullard, J. (2017) Can the presence of musculoskeletal pain be determined from the facial expressions of ridden horses (FEReq)? *J. Vet. Behav.: Clin. Appl. Res.* 19,78-89.

Dyson, S., Berger, J., Ellis, A., Mullard, J. (2018) Development of an ethogram for a pain scoring system in ridden horses and its application to determine the presence of musculoskeletal pain. *J. Vet. Behav.: Clin. Appl. Res.* 23, 47-57.

Dyson, S., Berger, J., Ellis, A., Mullard, J. (2018) Behavioural observations and comparisons of non-lame horses and lame horses before and after resolution of lameness by diagnostic analgesia. *J. Vet. Behav.: Clin. Appl. Res.* 26, 64-70.

Dyson, S., Ellis, A., Mullard, J., Berger, J. (2018) Response to Gleerup: understanding signals that indicate pain in ridden horses. J. *Vet. Behav.: Clin. Appl. Res.* 23, 87-90.

Dyson, S., Ellis, A., Quiney, L., Douglas, J., Bondi, A., Harris, P. (2018) The influence of rider: horse bodyweight ratio on equine gait, behaviour, response to thoracolumbar palpation and thoracolumbar dimensions: a pilot study. Proceedings of the 14th International Society of Equitation Science Congress, Rome, p120

Dyson, S., Van Dijk, J. (2020) Application of a ridden horse ethogram to video recordings of 21 horses before and after diagnostic analgesia: reduction in behaviour scores. *Equine Vet. Educ.* 32(S10), 104-111.

*Dyson, S., Pollard, D. (2020) Application of a Ridden Horse Pain Ethogram and its relationship with gait in a convenience sample of 60 riding horses. *Animals* 10, 1044. https://doi:10.3390/ani10061044

Dyson, S., Ellis, A., Guire, R., Douglas, J., Bondi, A., Harris, P. (2020) The influence of rider:horse bodyweight ratio and rider-horse-saddle-fit on equine gait and behaviour: a pilot study. *Equine Vet. Educ.* 32(10), 527-534. https://doi:10.1111/eve.13085;

Dyson, S., Thomson, K., Quiney, L., Bondi, A., Ellis, A. (2020) Can veterinarians reliably apply a whole horse ridden ethogram to differentiate non-lame and lame horses based on live horse assessment of behaviour? *Equine Vet. Educ.* 32(S10),112-120. https://doi:10.1111/eve.13104

Dyson, S., Ellis, A. (2022) Application of a Ridden Horse Pain Ethogram to horses competing at 5-star three-day-events: comparison with performance. *Equine Vet. Educ.* 34, 306-315. https://doi: 10.1111/eve.13415

Dyson, S. (2020) How to determine the presence of musculoskeletal pain in ridden horses by application of the Ridden Horse Pain Ethogram. *Proc. Amer. Assoc. Equine Pract.* 66, 334-342

Dyson, S., Bondi, A., Routh, J., Pollard, D. (2022) Gait abnormalities and ridden horse behaviour in a convenience sample of the United Kingdom ridden sports horse and leisure horse population. *Equine Vet. Educ.* 34, 84-95. https://doi: 10.1111/eve.13395

Dyson, S., Bondi, A., Routh, J., Pollard, D. (2022) Gait abnormalities and ridden horse behaviour in a convenience sample of the United Kingdom ridden sports horse and leisure horse population. *Equine Vet. Educ.* 34, 84-95. https://doi: 10.1111/eve.13395

Dyson, S., Martin, C., Bondi, A., Ellis, A. (2022) The influence of rider skill on ridden horse behaviour, assessed using the Ridden Horse Pain Ethogram, and gait quality. *Equine Vet. Educ.* 34(7), e308-e317. https://10.1111/eve.13434

Dyson, S., Bondi, A., Routh, J., Pollard, D., Preston, T., McConnell, C., Kydd, J. (2022) An investigation of behaviour during tacking-up and mounting in ridden sports and leisure horses. *Equine Vet. Educ.* 34, e258-267. https://doi: 10.1111/eve.13432

Dyson, S. (2022) The Ridden Horse Pain Ethogram. *Equine Vet. Educ.* 34(7), 372-380. https://doi: 10.1111/eve.13468

*Dyson, S., Pollard, D. (2021) Application of the Ridden Horse Pain Ethogram to elite dressage horses competing in World Cup Grand Prix Competitions. *Animals* 11, 1187. https://doi.org/0.3390/ani11051187

*Dyson, S., Pollard, D. (2021) Application of the Ridden Horse Pain Ethogram to horses competing at the Hickstead-Rotterdam Grand Prix Challenge and the British Dressage Grand Prix National Championship 2020 and comparison with World Cup Grand Prix competitions. *Animals* 11, 1820. https://doi.org/10.3390/ani11061820

Dyson, S. (2021) How to assess the suitability of rider size – height, morphology and weight – for optimal horse welfare and performance: a review. *Proc. Amer. Assoc. Equine Pract.* 67, 223-230

Dyson, S., Bondi, A., Routh, J., Kydd, J., Pollard, D. (2021) A review of how to recognise signs of abnormal equine behaviour during tacking-up and mounting and to understand their potential clinical significance. *Proc. Amer. Assoc. Equine Pract.* 67, 231-239

*Dyson, S., Pollard, D. (2022) Application of the Ridden Horse Pain

Ethogram to horses competing in British Eventing 90, 100 and Novice one-day events and comparison with performance. *Animals* 12, 590. https://doi.org/10.3390/ani12050590

Mullard, J., Berger, J., Ellis, A., Dyson, S. (2017) Development of an ethogram to describe facial expressions in ridden horses (FEReq). *J. Vet. Behav.: Clin. Appl. Res.* 18,7-12.

Thomson, K., Chan, C., Dyson, S. (2020) Head tossing behaviour in six horses: idiopathic headshaking or musculoskeletal pain? *Equine Vet. Educ.* 32(S11), 58-64.

Dyson, S. (2022) The Ridden Horse Pain Ethogram and the performance of sports horse: a review. *Proc Amer. Assoc. Equine Pract.* 68, 316-325.

*Dyson, S., Pollard, D. (2023) Application of the Ridden Horse Pain Ethogram to 150 horses with musculoskeletal pain before and after diagnostic anaesthesia. Animals 13: 1940. doi:10.3390/ani13121940

Index

 Matador

Made in the USA
Las Vegas, NV
10 April 2024